MW01051065

BIT BY BIT

SENIOR AUTHORS

Virginia A. Arnold   Carl B. Smith

AUTHORS

James Flood   Diane Lapp

LITERATURE CONSULTANTS

Joan I. Glazer   Margaret H. Lippert

Macmillan Publishing Company
New York

Collier Macmillan Publishers
London

ACKNOWLEDGMENTS

The publisher gratefully acknowledges permission to reprint the following copyrighted material:

"Alexander Calder: Just For the Fun of It" by Gail Tuchman ". . . so I made a circus just for the fun of it. . ." comes from THE ARTIST'S VOICE: Talks with Seventeen Artists by Katharine Kuh. Copyright © 1960, 1961, 1962 by Katharine Kuh. Used by permission of Harper & Row, Publishers, Inc. "I want to make things that are fun to look at." From CONVERSATIONS WITH ARTISTS by Selden Rodman. Copyright © 1957 by Selden Rodman. Published by The Devin-Adair Company and used with their permission.

"The Best Train Set Ever" from THE BEST TRAIN SET EVER by Pat Hutchins. Copyright © 1978 by Pat Hutchins. By permission of Greenwillow Books (A Division of William Morrow & Company) and The Bodley Head, London.

"Best Wishes, Ed" (text only) from WINSTON, NEWTON, ELTON, AND ED by James Stevenson. Copyright © 1978 by James Stevenson. Adapted by permission of Greenwillow Books (A Division of William Morrow & Company).

"The Cobbler's" is excerpted from "The Cobbler's" from the book TAXIS AND TOAD STOOLS by Rachel Field. Copyright © 1926 by The Women's Educational and Industrial Union. Reprinted by permission of Doubleday & Co., Inc.

"Flags for Sale" is adapted from "Flags for Sale" from LEO AND EMILY'S BIG IDEAS by Franz Brandenberg. Illustrations by Aliki Brandenberg. Text copyright © 1982 by Franz Brandenberg. Illustrations copyright © 1982 by Aliki Brandenberg. By permission of Greenwillow Books (A Division of William Morrow & Company) and The Bodley Head, London.

"Gloria Who Might Be My Best Friend" is an adaptation of text only from p. 58–71 of THE STORIES JULIAN TELLS by Ann Cameron. Copyright © 1981 by Ann Cameron. Adapted by permission of Pantheon Books, a division of Random House, Inc.

"Jasper Makes Music" is from JASPER MAKES MUSIC by Betty Horvath. Copyright © 1967 by Franklin Watts, Inc. Used by permission of the publisher.

"I'm up here" is Poem #13 from ANY ME I WANT TO BE, Poems by Karla Kuskin. Copyright © 1972 by Karla Kuskin. All rights reserved. Reprinted by permission of Harper & Row, Publishers, Inc.

"M and M and the Big Bag" from M AND M AND THE BIG BAG by Pat Ross. Copyright © 1981 by Pat Ross. Reprinted by permission of Pantheon Books, a division of Random House, Inc.

Parts of this work were published in the first edition of CONNECTIONS.
This work is also published in individual volumes under the titles *Many Messages* and *Pennies and Presents*, copyright © 1989 Macmillan Publishing Company, a division of Macmillan, Inc.

Macmillan Publishing Company
866 Third Avenue
New York, N.Y. 10022
Collier Macmillan Canada, Inc.

Printed in the United States of America.

ISBN 0-02-174820-9

9 8 7 6 5 4 3

Cover Design: John Sanford   **Unit Openers:** Bob Shein
Feature Logos and Medallion Logos: Eva Vagreti Cockrille
ILLUSTRATION CREDITS: Sal Murdocca, 3–8; Debbie Pinkney, 10–18; Patti Boyd, 22–32; Bob Shein, 34–35; Janet Bohn, 44, 45, 114, 115, 156, 186, 187, 210, 265–296; Sally Springer, 46–54; Ellen Appleby, 56–57; Carlos Freire, 58–68; Jan Pyk, 71; Karen Loccisano, 72–79; Bob Radigan, 81; Elliot Kreloff, 82–90; Allan Eitzen, 94–102; Patricia Henderson Lincoln, 134–135; Diana Magnuson, 138–146; Mac Evans, 176–177; Sheryl Arneman, 178–184; John Nez, 188–198; Gary Zamchick, 188–189, 191; Doreen Gay-Kassel, 212–222; Steve Peringer, 224–225; Fredric Winkowski, 226–234; Wendy Edelson, 236–237; Joel Snyder, 250–262; Linda Solovic, 298–310.
PHOTO CREDITS: © Clara Aich, 138, 141 (4-inset), 143 (3-inset), 145 (5-inset). Courtesy Al Davidson, 141T, B, 143T, B, 145. © Lawrence Hutchins, 174. © Peggy Jarrell Kaplan, 70. © Ken Lax, 158 to 161, 202 to 208. © Cyane B. Lowden/Science Museum of Virginia, 162. MAGNUM PHOTOS: © Inge Morath, 116. © Blair Seitz, 36 to 42. SHOSTAL ASSOCIATES: © Gerard Fritz, 148–149. Collection of WHITNEY MUSEUM OF AMERICAN ART: Alexander Calder. *Chock.* (1972). Metal assemblage. 11x28x22 inches. Gift of the artist. Acq. #72.55, 117; *Kangaroo* from the *Circus.* (1926–31). Metal, wood and wire. 5½x8x3¼ inches. Acq. #83.36.6, 118B; *Clown* from the *Circus.* (1926–31). Wire, painted wood, cloth, yarn, leather, metal and button. 10½x9x4 inches. Acq. #83.36.3, 120TL; *Lion and Cage* from the *Circus.* (1926–31). Wire, yarn, cloth and buttons. 9½x16½x5 inches. (lion). Painted wood, wire, cloth, cork and bottle caps. 17⅛x19½x17½ inches. (cage). Acq. #83.36a-b, 120TR; *Seals* from the *Circus.* (1926–31). Painted wood, metal, wire, cork and plastic ball. 8x19⅝x5 inches. Acq. #83.36.10, 120B; *Big Bug.* 1970. Gouache on paper. 29⅛x42¾ inches. Promised gift of Howard and Jean Lipman. Acq. #P.40.80, 121. © Allen Yarinsky, 122. Collection of Nanette Hayes Saxton, Alexander Calder. *Circus,* 1926, oil on burlap, 69x83 inches. On extended loan to University Art Museum, Berkeley, California, 118T. Collection of WHITNEY MUSEUM OF AMERICAN ART: Purchase, with funds from a public fundraising campaign in May 1982. One half the funds were contributed by the Robert Wood Johnson Jr. Charitable Trust. Additional major donations were given by The Lauder Foundation; the Robert Lehman Foundation, Inc.; The Howard and Jean Lipman Foundation, Inc.; an anonymous donor; The T.M. Evans Foundation, Inc.; MacAndrews & Forbes Group, Incorporated; the De Witt Wallace Fund; Martin and Agneta Gruss; Anne Phillips; Mr. and Mrs. Laurence S. Rockefeller; the Simon Foundation, Inc.; Marylou Whitney; Bankers Trust Company; Mr. and Mrs. Kenneth N. Dayton; Joel and Anne Ehrenkranz; Irvin and Kenneth Feld; Flora Whitney Miller. More than 500 individuals from 26 states and abroad also contributed to the campaign. 83.36, 118B, 120.

Contents

5

6

Introducing Level 6

UNIT

MANY MESSAGES

1

You send and get messages every day. Wave hello, tell someone your name, write a letter —all are messages. In this unit, you will read about finding messages in a secret code, a book, a name, a letter, the tail of a kite, and a piece of art. How can messages help people share and learn?

The more that you read,
the more things you will know.
The more that you learn,
the more places you'll go.

Dr. Seuss

atchway utoway orfay hetay iantgay odecay

The Code Toad

A code is a kind of message. Tim finds that a code is a way to get to know new people. These new friends want to crack the code. Read to find out what a Code Toad is.

It was Tim's first day in his new school. Tim listened to the teacher call out every name. That was how he came to know that the boy who sat next to him was Scott. Tim looked at Scott. If he could have one wish, it would be to have Scott for a friend.

10

When the boys and girls went out to the playground, some of them had a soccer ball to kick. Scott and a boy called Jason picked nine players, but they didn't want Tim on their team.

"We don't need more players," they said. "We have all we want now."

Tim could play soccer. He was even very good at it, but they didn't let him show them. He hated to just watch.

Just before the game was over, the ball came Tim's way.

"Look out!" shouted Jason as he ran to stop the ball. Tim was in his way and Jason banged into him. Then they heard the teacher call out that it was time to go inside. The game was over. Because of Tim, it was a bad day for Jason.

It was a bad day for Tim, too. When he got on the bus to go home he walked by some of the boys from his room. No one asked him to sit with them. So he sat in the back and listened while they shouted to one another. Seeing them have so much fun, Tim felt sad inside. He hated this new school.

Tim walked home from the bus stop. His bag full of books felt so heavy. When he came inside, his mother asked, "Why do you look so sad?"

"Nobody would play with me in school," Tim told her. "They all have friends and they don't want to make a new one."

"It was your first day. Give them a little time to get to know you," his mother told him. "I know things will change."

"That isn't much help now," thought Tim. Tim sat down and began to read one of the books his grandmother gave him.

He sat on the creaking steps in front
of his house and read and read. The book
had a secret way to write called code.

There were all kinds. Tim began to try
them out. At first he could only say one
word in code at a time. He had to work at
it until he could say a full sentence in
code. Soon he could say anything he
wanted. It was like a game.

Before school the next day, he put a secret message on Scott's chair. It said—

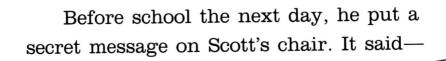

atchway utoay orfay hetay iantgay odecay oadtay!

Seeing the message, Scott's friends wanted to know what it said.

"It's in code, but I know how to read it," Scott told them. "It says—**WATCH OUT FOR THE GIANT CODE TOAD.**"

"But who is this from?" asked a boy.

Scott said he still didn't know who it was.

That night Tim thought of another code. He had to stay up late to plan it. After he thought it all out he began to draw. It was like a crossword game.

**IF YOU CAN READ
THIS SECRET MESSAGE
YOU CAN BE A CODE TOAD.**

Before school the next day, Tim began to slide a new message on every chair in his room. When the boys and girls saw that the Code Toad was back again, they laughed.

"Is this some kind of a joke?" Jason asked Scott.

"I don't know," said Scott. "But this is fun. I would like to know who the Code Toad is."

Tim listened to them. It felt good to hear what they said. Tim couldn't wait to see if someone would find out what the message said.

Again, Scott was the only one who could read the message and he just had to find out who made the code. All of a sudden, he had a plan of his own.

When Scott got home after school he called Jason. "I think I know how to trap the Code Toad," he said.

The next day there was another message on every chair. This time, to Tim's surprise, there was even one for him. It looked like this—

Tim read it one way. It didn't mean anything to him. Then he read it another way. It didn't make sense at all. At last he thought of how it went. He only read a word with one black cat after it. Now it read—

REPORT TO THE GYM AFTER SCHOOL

At last school was over. All day Tim had waited to find out who or what would be in front of the gym. To his surprise it was Scott.

"Are you the Black Cat?" he asked.

"If you are the Code Toad," said Scott. "You were the only one who could read my message," Scott told him. "So it could only be you." He laughed. "I thought it was you all along."

Tim laughed, too. "That was a good trick."

"Why don't we try it again?" said Scott. "We can work out another code right now."

"Good!" said Tim. "We can do it at my house. I have a code book."

They had to run for their bus. Now Tim's heavy bag felt light.

Thinking and Writing About the Selection

1. What was Tim's one wish?

2. What did Tim's first secret message say?

3. Do you think it was hard for Tim not to tell that he was the Code Toad? Why?

4. Why did Tim's heavy bag feel light after he met the Black Cat?

Applying the Key Skill
Inflectional Endings

Number your paper from 1 to 3. Read the sentences below and look at the words underneath each sentence. Then write the word that would complete each sentence on your paper.

1. Jason is the ___ soccer player on the team.
   a. faster   b. fastest

2. Tim is the ___ boy in school.
   a. newer   b. newest

3. This code is ___ than the last one.
   a. harder   b. hardest

SKILLS activity

SEQUENCE OF EVENTS

Most stories have a plan. In the plan the things that take place in the story are told in some kind of order. Words like **first**, **next**, and **last** show the order. Words like **second**, **third**, and **after** can show order, too. When you read look for these words and think about the order.

ACTIVITY A Read this story about Tim. Think about the plan of the story. Then write the answer to each question on your paper. Use complete sentences.

Tim hated his first day in school. First he watched the boys and girls play soccer, but he didn't play. Then, on the way home, he didn't have a friend to sit with him. When he got home, he thought of something he could do to make some friends.

1. What did Tim do first at school?
2. What did Tim do last in the story?
3. What words helped you know the order of the plan?

20

ACTIVITY B Read the story and think about its plan. Then read the sentences below the story.

Jane wanted to have an aquarium. The first thing she did was to get an aquarium, plants, and some fish. After she got home, she put water in the aquarium. Next, she put in the plants and her fish. Then Jane gave the fish some food. Jane was happy with her new aquarium.

Jane put fish in the aquarium.
Jane got an aquarium.
Jane put in the water.
Jane gave food to the fish.

1. Write the sentence that tells what Jane did first.
2. Then write the sentence that tells what Jane did last.
3. Write the words in the story that show you the order Jane did things.

I DON'T LIKE READING

Virginia Arnold

Bets loved to skate and play soccer. But she didn't like to read . . . until she met Owl and Caterpillar. They have a message for Bets.

"It's time to read, Bets," said Mother.

"But I haven't tried my brand new skates yet," said Bets. She skated to the street.

"Betty Anne, come here now!" cried Mother.

When Mother spoke like that, it was a sign to move—and move quickly. Bets skated back to the porch.

"After you read for a while, you can try your new skates," Mother said.

"Do I have to read the whole book?" asked Bets.

"Oh, Bets!" said Mother. "You may like this book. You picked it out at the library. I'll read with you," she said.

Just as they sat down on the porch steps, Bets's brother came out to say there was a call for Mother.

"Bets, read your book until I get back," said Mother. "Then I'll read with you." Mother ran into the house.

The porch was so hot. Bets's eyes felt heavy. She made a face at the book. She loved to skate and swim. She loved to play soccer, but she hated to read. Her mother was a librarian and loved to read. And so did her father. Her brother loved to read so much that he worked at the library after school.

"Why am I the only one in the family who doesn't like to read?" she thought.

"How would I know?" whispered a little voice. "Have you tried to like reading?"

"She could be tired," said a gruff voice. "She looks bad to me, but then anything that doesn't have feathers looks bad to me."

Bets opened her eyes wide. "Who said that?" she asked.

"Who said what?" said the little voice. "There are two of us you know."

"I spoke second," said the gruff voice. "Caterpillar spoke first. You spoke third."

"Who are you?" asked Bets. "Where are you?"

"We are right here. Open the book a little," said a little voice.

Bets opened the book. There was a picture of a caterpillar and an owl. As she looked, the owl suddenly said, "Come in! Come in! It's hot when you hold the book open like that!"

Bets never did know how she did it, but there she was, on a chair, in a little house with an owl and a caterpillar looking at her.

"This whole thing is silly," cried Bets. "How did I get here?"

"I asked you in," said the owl. "And in you came," said Caterpillar. "Now back to what we were saying. Have you tried to like reading? Why don't you like reading?"

"I don't know," said Bets.

"You must know," said Owl. "You are the one who doesn't like it. Now as for me, I love to read."

"I can take it or leave it," Caterpillar said. "Do you know how to read?"

"Yes," said Bets, "I just don't like it. I just don't see why I need to read. I watch TV and learn things."

Owl said, "When you watch TV, people tell you what to learn. When you read, you can pick anything you want to learn. You can find a book about anything you want to know."

"I never thought of it that way," said Bets.

Caterpillar cried, "Owl, I think we can help her with a 'show her what reading is for' trip!"

"Oh, no," said Owl. "First, I am tired. Second, I might miss lunch . . ."

"And third," said Caterpillar, "you know you love it. Come on."

"What is going on?" asked Bets.

"Just get on my back and be quiet," said Owl. "I must be back in time for lunch and my nap or I get very cross. If people had feathers, I would not mind so much!"

"Hold on! One, two, three! Away we go!" shouted Caterpillar.

In a second, they flew out toward a sign by the sea.

"Can you read that?" asked Caterpillar.

"Do not swim! Sharks!" read Bets.

"If you couldn't read and went for a swim there, you would be a shark dinner," said Caterpillar.

"I never thought of that," said Bets.

They flew over a desert. "See that man reading a map? If he couldn't read, he might never find water," said Owl. Then, they flew down to a library.

"Books can help you do the things you like to do better," said Caterpillar. "Here are three books. These two could help you play soccer better. This third one is about a girl who likes to skate."

"Let me look," cried Bets.

"Not now," said Owl. "We have a good deal more to see and I feel lunch coming on."

They flew on and went to hear a storyteller tell a story. Just as the tiger was going to eat the boy, Owl said, "Come on. We must go."

"But I want to hear the whole story," cried Bets.

"It is in the library, but you never read it," said Caterpillar.

In a second, they were back at the little house. Owl said, "It's time for you to go. We don't have lunch for three."

Bets said, "Don't you want to know if I like reading now?"

Caterpillar said, "Only you can make up your mind about that."

Bets said, "I never thought reading made so much sense. I never thought about why people needed to read."

"If you had feathers, you might think more," said Owl as he walked out of the room.

"Don't mind him," said Caterpillar.

"Good luck," Owl called as he flew away.

Tap, tap, tap. Three drops of water fell on Bets. "Wait," she called to her friends. "Do you know water is coming in your roof? Wait! Wait!"

"Bets, Bets, Bets! Wake up and come in out of the rain," called Mother for the third time. "You will get soaking wet."

Bets opened her eyes. Here she was on her own porch at her own house. She looked quickly at her book, but the owl and caterpillar didn't move.

She ran up the steps into the house.

"Mother," she called. "Do I have a story for you! And it's about reading!"

Thinking and Writing About the Selection

1. Where did Bets get the book that her mother wanted her to read?

2. What things did Bets like to do?

3. Why did Owl think it was better to read than to watch TV?

4. Why do you think Bets liked the 'show her what reading is for' trip?

Applying the Key Skill
Realism and Fantasy

Write these headings on your paper.

    Real   Make-Believe

Write each sentence under the right heading.

1. Bets and her mother read a book on the porch steps.

2. Bets sits in a small house and talks with an owl and a caterpillar.

3. Mother calls Bets to come into the house and eat lunch.

4. Bets gets on Owl's back and they fly toward the sea.

Reading

A story is a special thing.
The ones that I have read,
They do not stay inside the books.
They stay inside my head.

Marchette Chute

AT THE LIBRARY

Marlyn Mangus

Bets began to use the library after she met Owl and Caterpillar. You, too, may want to use the library to find something to read, or something to do.

Books, books, and more books! That may be how you think of a library. The word *library* comes from a very old word for "book." A library is a collection of books.

A library may be little or big. You and your family may have a little library at home. A home library has books you like. It may have books you use to find information, too.

A school library is big. It has books to
help you with your school work. Your
school library may be called a media center.
A media center has other things, as well as
books. It may have records, a picture to
look at, or a game to play.

A public library is for all of us. It is a very big collection of books of all kinds. People of every age can use it. Some people go to the library for books of stories they want to read. Other people may go there to look up information. Still other people go to the library to read through magazines and newspapers. No one has to pay money to use the library.

A library may have a huge number of books. Where is each one put? In a library, one kind of book is put with other books of the same kind. Story books are all put in one place. Information books are put in other places. The librarian can show you where to find each kind of book.

A book may have information about owls, elephants, plants, or computers. Some books have information about all kinds of things. You can find information quickly in these books. This picture shows some of these information books. Can you name them?

Did you know that you can take some library books home? To do this, you have to have a library card. Your library may let you have a card when you can sign your own name.

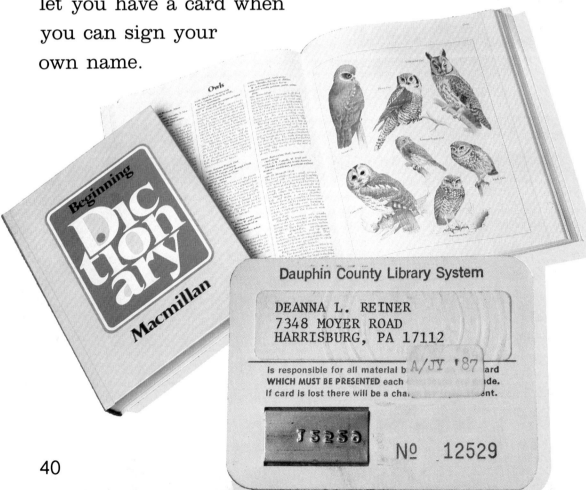

Take your library card and the book you want to the librarian. A date will be put on a card inside the book. You have to bring the book back on or before that date. If you forget and don't bring it back, there will be a fine. A fine is money you have to pay if you keep a book too long.

A public library may have more than story and information books. Newspapers and magazines help people keep up with what is going on. A library may have books in Braille for people who are blind. It may have computers you can use to find information. It has things for people of every age.

There is more to do at a library than just read. There may be a storyteller or someone to read stories to boys and girls one day. You may watch a show on another day. There may be people who will tell you how to make things or do things.

One last word: when you go through a library, you may see signs that say, "QUIET, PLEASE." A library is a place for whispers. When you whisper, you don't bother the other people who have come there to read and work.

A library is a place where you can learn and have fun, too. There are books to read and things to do. It is a good place to know about.

Thinking and Writing About the Selection

1. Why do people use the library?

2. Who will help you find things in the library?

3. Tell why the sign in the library says, "QUIET, PLEASE."

 4. What would you like to do at the library?

Applying the Key Skill
Recall Details

Think about the story you have just read. Then complete the sentences with the correct answer on your paper.

1. A library is ___.

    a. a game to play

    b. a collection of books

2. Along with books, some libraries also have ___.

    a. records and games to play

    b. a place to skate

3. If you have a library card, you can ___.

    a. get a librarian to help you

    b. take a book home with you

SKILLS activity

RECALL DETAILS

The stories we read all have a main idea. But stories also have many facts that tell about the people, animals, places, and things that happen in the story. As you read, think about the facts and try to remember them.

ACTIVITY A Read the paragraph below. Then complete each sentence. Write the sentences on your paper.

Bets was late for her soccer game at the park. She put on her skates. She put her soccer ball in a bag. She skated to the park. Bets got there just in time for the game.

1. Bets had to get _____.
   home
   to a soccer game
   to school

2. She put on her _____.
   shoes
   skates
   socks

3. The soccer game was _____.

    at school

    at the library

    at the park

4. She put _____ in her bag.

    a soccer ball

    her skates

    a book

ACTIVITY B Read the paragraph about owls. Then write the answers to the questions on your paper. Use complete sentences.

Have you ever seen an owl? Owls live in the woods. They have big eyes, feathers and a little tail. Owls sleep in the day. At night they look for food. An owl might find a mouse, a frog, or a bug to eat. When an owl is flying, it can't be heard.

1. Where do owls live?
2. What do owls look like?
3. When do owls sleep?
4. What do owls do at night?
5. What do owls eat?

The Name Day

Gibbs Davis

Maria

Sonja
Adrienne

Nam...

Alexandra

You can find a book of names at the library.
What does your name mean? Would you
change your name for a day if you could?
Read and find out what Mei-Lan and Mary
think of their names.

Mary never liked her name. In every school it was the same thing. There were too many Marys. Her mother and father shouldn't have called her Mary in the first place. Thanks to them, she was just another name.

All afternoon Mary had sat alone in the library trying to think of a new name.

She wished she lived someplace like Mexico. Then, her name would be MARIA. Smiling, Mary picked up one of her best pencils and wrote MARIA. It looked good on paper, much better than just Mary.

Mary watched the new girl in school walk into the library alone.

"Hi, Mei-Lan," said Ms. Bloom, the school librarian. Mei-Lan asked Ms. Bloom for a book.

When Mei-Lan got the book she wanted, she carried it over to where Mary was and sat down. After looking through it, she began to write very quickly.

Mei-Lan, what a pretty name, thought Mary. Some people have all the luck. Before Mary could say anything, the girl had walked out the door. On her way out, Mei-Lan had dropped her book.

When Mary picked up the book on the floor, her eyes opened wide with surprise. It was a book of names!

Mary carried her things outside to wait for the school bus home. When she saw Mei-Lan by the bus stop she walked over to meet her.

"Hi, my name is Mary."

The girl looked up. "I would do anything to have a name like Mary," said Mei-Lan. "I was trying to find a new name in the library this afternoon."

"I know," said Mary. She gave Mei-Lan back her book of names. "This fell on the floor."

"Thanks," whispered Mei-Lan.

"Mei-Lan is so pretty," said Mary, smiling. "I think it's the best girl's name in our whole school."

"You do?" said Mei-Lan.

Just then the bus came up the street.

The girls ran to meet the bus. "Please sit next to me," said Mary.

Mei-Lan sat down next to Mary. She had just made her first friend.

The next afternoon, Mary and Mei-Lan
saw a big paper sign outside the library.
It read:

NAME DAY
Come to the school library this afternoon
for a report about Name Day.

"Name Day. What is that?" asked
Mei-Lan.

"Well, there is one way to find out," said
Mary, as she opened the library door.

Inside, Ms. Bloom spoke to a room full
of people.

"How many of us at one time have
wished for a brand new first name? Hold up
your hand if you have."

One hand after another went up.

"I didn't know so many people felt as we
do," whispered Mei-Lan.

Ms. Bloom went on. "I thought we could try something new. On Name Day you can each pick out a new name, and the whole school will call you by that name for a full day.

"Try to pick a name that will mean something to you. Look at your family tree. Ask your mother and father why they gave you your name. Think about it."

The next afternoon Mary carried her pencils and paper outside. She was going to meet Mei-Lan at the playground. Thanks to Mei-Lan and her book, they were going to have the best names in school.

Just then Mary saw Mei-Lan. She was walking so quickly that the tops of her feet spun on the ice. "We have to get to work," said Mei-Lan. She sat down and opened the name book. As she read the names out loud, Mary wrote them all down on paper. There were first and last names, boys and girls names, and even family names.

When it was time to go back inside, Mary's head spun with names. "I never thought I would say this, but I am tired of names."

"I know what you mean," said Mei-Lan.

On Name Day, Mary walked through school. She wanted to show off her name tag. It read: ALEXANDRA.

She wanted to show her new name to Mei-Lan. She rushed into the library to find her.

"You have to hear this," whispered Mary.

"Don't you want to know my new name first?" asked Mei-Lan.

"Yes," said Mary.

"You won't tease me?" asked Mei-Lan.

"No," said Mary.

Mei-Lan showed her name tag. It read MARY!

Suddenly Mary felt glad.

Name Day was so much fun Mary and Mei-Lan hated to leave school. They were the last people to get on the bus home.

"Did you look up your name in the library?" asked Mary.

"Yes," said Mei-Lan and showed Mary another book of names. "It says Mei-Lan is the same as Pretty Flower."

Mary thought of all the other Marys on her street. "I wish my name could mean something, too." She looked sad.

"It does mean something," said Mei-Lan. "It means something to me."

"What?" asked Mary.

"Best friend," said Mei-Lan smiling, and she put away her book of names.

Thinking and Writing About the Selection

1. Why didn't Mary like her name?

2. What did Ms. Bloom tell the children they would do on Name Day?

3. Why do you think Mary picked the name Alexandra for Name Day?

4. Do you think that Mary likes her name better now than she did before?

Applying the Key Skill
Initial Consonant Clusters

Use the letters below to finish the words. Write the sentences on your paper.

    sm   sp   sk   sc

1. One day Mary looked out the door, and the ___y was blue!

2. Winter was over and Mary didn't need to wear her ___arf and hat. She stopped to ___ell a flower on her way to Mei-Lan's house.

3. Soon Mary and Mei-Lan would ___in on their skates!

My Other Name

Jennifer's my other name
    (It's make-believe
    and just a game.)

I'm really Anne,
But just the same
I'd much
    much
    rather
    have a name
    like Jennifer.

    (So, if you can
    don't call me Anne.)

Myra Cohn Livingston

Rumpelstiltskin

Retold by Margaret H. Lippert

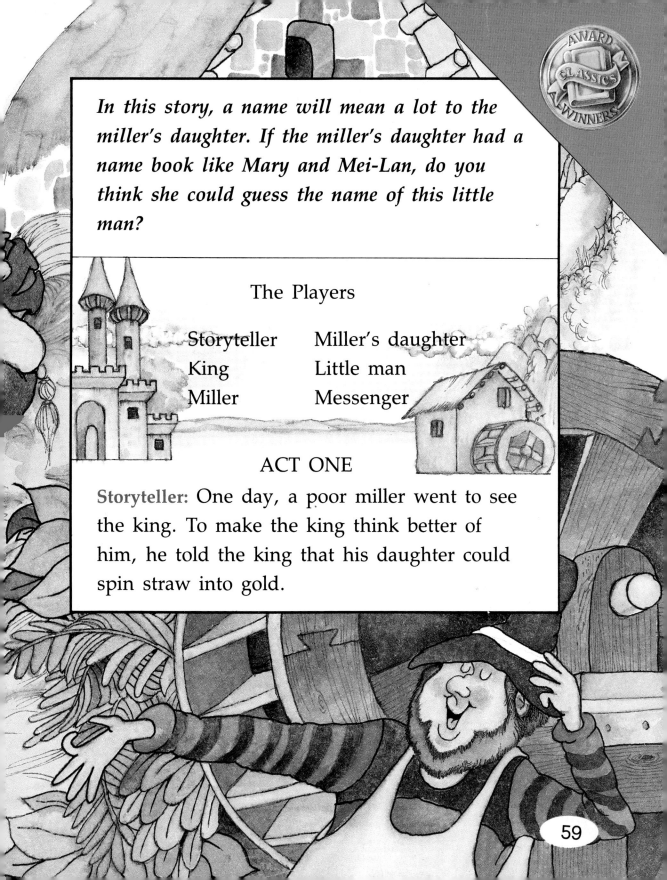

In this story, a name will mean a lot to the miller's daughter. If the miller's daughter had a name book like Mary and Mei-Lan, do you think she could guess the name of this little man?

The Players

Storyteller	Miller's daughter
King	Little man
Miller	Messenger

ACT ONE

Storyteller: One day, a poor miller went to see the king. To make the king think better of him, he told the king that his daughter could spin straw into gold.

King: I do not know anyone who can spin straw into gold. I would like to meet your daughter. Tell her to come and see me.

Miller: I will tell her the king wishes to see her. She will be here in the morning.

Storyteller: That night, the miller told his daughter what the king had said. The next morning, she went to the king's castle.

King (sternly): Your father said that you can spin straw into gold. Now I will see if what he said is true. Here is a room full of straw, and a spinning wheel. Spin all this straw into gold, or in the morning you will die.

Storyteller: The king went away. The girl was alone in the room full of straw. She did not know how to spin straw into gold. Because she was scared of what would happen to her, she began to cry. Just then, a little man came in.

Little man: What is the matter?

Miller's daughter: I have to spin this straw into gold. I do not know how to do it, and I am scared of what will happen to me.

Little man: What will you give me if I spin it for you?

Miller's daughter: I will give you my necklace.

Storyteller: The girl gave the little man her necklace. Then the little man sat down at the spinning wheel and began to spin the straw into gold. When he had spun all of the straw into gold, he went away. In the morning, the king came back.

King (as he takes some of the gold in his hands): GOLD! This is gold. So what your father said was true. I did not know anyone could spin straw into gold.

Storyteller: The king led the miller's daughter to another room.

King: Here is another room, with more straw than the first. I want you to spin all this straw into gold, too. If you do not spin it all into gold by morning, you will die.

Storyteller: Again the girl was alone. Again she began to cry, and again the little man came in.

Little man: Now what is the matter?

Miller's daughter: I have to spin all this straw into gold, too.

Little man: What will you give me if I spin it for you?

Miller's daughter: I will give you my ring.

Storyteller: The girl gave the little man her ring, and he began to spin. Before long, he had spun all of the straw into gold. Then he went away. In the morning, the king came back.

King: This time you did even better! I have one more room full of straw. If you spin that straw into gold, I will make you my queen.

Storyteller: After the king went away, the girl began to cry. For the third time, the little man came in.

Little man: What will you give me if I spin the straw for you this time?

Miller's daughter: I have nothing more to give.

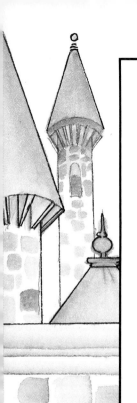

Little man: Then give me the first child you have after you are queen.

Storyteller: The poor girl did not know what to do, but at last she told the little man he could have her first child. By morning, he had spun all the straw into gold. Then he went away, and the king came in.

King: You did it again! Now you will be my queen.

Storyteller: So that very morning, the king made the miller's daughter his queen.

Storyteller: The king and queen were very happy, and after some time they had a baby. Suddenly one day the little man came to the happy queen.

Queen: (sternly): What are you doing here?

Little man: Did you forget so soon? When I helped you spin straw into gold, you said you would give me your first child. Now I have come for the child.

Queen: I can't give you our child. I will give you all the gold in the kingdom, but please let us keep our child.

Little man: I do not want gold. I only want what you said I could have, your first child.

Storyteller: The queen felt so sad that she began to cry.

Little man: I do not like to see you so sad. If you can guess my name, I will let you keep your baby. But if after three days you can't guess my name, you will have to give your baby to me.

Storyteller: The queen was up all night thinking of names. In the morning, the little man came.

Little man: Can you guess my name?

Queen: Is it Tom?

Little man: No!

Queen: Is it Harry?

Little man: No!

Storyteller: The queen went on and on but she could not guess his name. The same day, the queen asked all her friends to tell her all the names they had heard. The second morning the little man came again, but still she could not guess his name. Then the queen asked a messenger to come to her.

Queen: I need new names. I have one more morning to guess the name of the little man. Go as quickly as you can, and ask all the people you see to tell you all the names they know.

Storyteller: The messenger came back late that night, and told the queen all the names that the people had told him.

Queen: Is that all?

Messenger: That is all the names people told me, but I did hear one more name. As the sun went down in the woods, I saw a little house made of mud and sticks by the path. In front of the house there was a little man. He was laughing and I heard him say:

> Soon I'll bring the queen's child here
> She will never win my game
> For no one in the kingdom knows
> That Rumpelstiltskin is my name.

Storyteller: In the morning the little man came for the last time.

Little man: Can you guess my name?

Queen: Is it Ebenezer?

Little man: No!

Queen: Is it Spindleshank?

Little man: No!

Queen: Is it . . . Rumpelstiltskin?

Little man: Who told you that? Who told you that?

Storyteller: The little man was so mad that he jumped into the ground until not even his head could be seen, and no one saw him again.

Thinking and Writing About the Selection

1. What did the miller tell the king?

2. What two things did the miller's daughter give the little man?

3. Do you think the miller should have told the king that his daughter could spin straw into gold? Why?

 4. Do you think Rumpelstiltskin was a good helper? Why?

Applying the Key Skill
Context Clues

Find the meaning of the underlined word.
Write the word and its meaning on your paper.

1. Rumpelstiltskin <u>raced</u> by the miller's daughter to get to the spinning wheel.
   a. ran   b. blew   c. banged

2. The King and Queen ate their <u>meal</u> at the miller's house last night.
   a. chairs   b. dinner   c. turtle

3. The little girl began to <u>pull</u> on her mother's hand.
   a. open   b. trick   c. tug

Margaret H. Lippert

There are three kinds of stories I like to tell: true stories about funny or interesting things that happen to people in my family, folk tales, and stories I make up, that no one has ever heard, or thought of before.

I love to tell stories and to write them down. When I am asked to write a story I feel scared because I don't know how to begin, and I feel excited because I know I will live that story for a while.

As a writer, I don't know who my words will reach. That is why I find being an author so thrilling. I don't know you, but now you know a little about me, just by reading these words. I like that.

TIME FOR A RHYME

Read what the messenger hears the little man say in the folk tale "Rumpelstiltskin."

> Soon I'll bring the queen's child here
> She will never win my <u>game</u>
> For no one in the kingdom knows
> That Rumpelstiltskin is my <u>name</u>.

Look at the words with a line under them. Say the words, *game* and *name.* These words sound alike. They have the same vowel and ending sound.

Read the sentence parts below. Match the parts so the last words rhyme and make a sentence.

1. A day in the sun   if you are hot.
2. This is the spot   can be so much fun.

Can you think of some words to rhyme with these words? Can you write sentences with parts that rhyme?

> spun   best   ring   code

71

Gloria Who Might Be My Best Friend

Anne Cameron

Julian does not try to guess the new girl's
name. He finds out that one way to find out
the name of someone new is just to ask,
"Who are you?" That someone new may be
a friend.

72

If you have a girl for a friend, people find out and laugh at you. That's why I didn't want a girl for a friend—not until I met Gloria.

One day I saw a van a block from my house. A man was bringing in chairs and tables and books and boxes. I watched for a while, and suddenly I heard a voice.

"Who are you?"

I looked and there was a girl in red. She looked the same age as me. She had two braids.

"I am Julian," I said. "Who are you?"

"I am Gloria," she said. "I come from Newport. Can you do a cartwheel?"

She spun sideways and did two cartwheels on the grass.

I never did a cartwheel before. I wanted to
do one like Gloria's. My hands went down in the
grass, my feet went up and I fell over.

I looked at Gloria to see if she was laughing
at me. If she was laughing at me, I was going to
go home and forget about her.

But she just looked at me and said, "You have
to keep trying again and again," and then I liked her.

"I know where there is a bird's nest in your
yard," I said.

"Where?" Gloria asked.

I showed her where a robin lives. Gloria
jumped up on the tree and looked in.

"Would you like to come over to my house?" I asked.

"All right," Gloria said, "if it is all right with my mother."

It was all right, so Gloria and I went to my house, and I showed her my games and my rock collection.

"I wish you would live here a long time," I told Gloria.

"I wish I would, too." Gloria said, "I know the best way to make wishes,"

"What is that?" I asked.

"First you make a kite. Do you know how to make one?"

"Yes," I said. "I know how to make good kites because my father showed me. We make them out of two crossed sticks and some newspapers."

We went out into the yard and made a kite. I tied on the kite string and got rags for the tail.

"Do you have some paper and two pencils?" Gloria asked. "Because now we make the wishes."

I didn't know what she was going to do, but I went in the house and got pencils and paper.

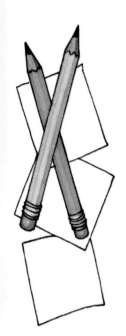

"All right," Gloria said. "Every wish you want to have come true you write down on paper. You don't tell me your wishes, and I don't tell you mine. If you tell, your wishes don't come true."

Gloria sat down on the ground again and began to write her wishes. I wanted to see what they were—but I went to another place in the yard and wrote my own wishes. I wrote:

1. I wish I could play soccer better than anyone.
2. I wish I could ride in a plane.
3. I wish Gloria would stay here and be my best friend.

I went over to Gloria with my wishes in my hand.

"How many wishes did you make?" Gloria asked.

"Three," I said. "How many did you make?"

"Two," Gloria said.

I wanted to know what they were.

"Now we put the wishes on the tail of the kite," Gloria said. "Every time we tie a rag on the tail, we place a wish in it."

I tied mine in, and then Gloria tied in hers, and we carried the kite into the yard.

"You hold the tail," Gloria said, "and I will tug."

We ran to the open yard by the house.

The kite began to move up into the sky. Soon the kite was flying over the roof of my house and was floating toward the sun.

"When we take the kite down," Gloria said, "there shouldn't be one wish in the tail. When the wind takes all your wishes, that's when you know it's going to work."

The kite stayed up for a long time. The kite looked like a little black dot in the sun.

"Can we take it in?" I asked.

"All right," Gloria said.

The kite came down and down until it fell at our feet.

We looked at the tail. The wishes were not there.

Could it be that I would get to be good at soccer and have a ride in a plane? And Gloria would be my best friend?

"Gloria," I said, "did you wish we would be friends?"

"You should not ask me that!" Gloria laughed.

"I know," I said. But inside I was smiling. I guessed one thing Gloria wished for, that we would be best friends.

Thinking and Writing About the Selection

1. What would Julian do if Gloria laughed at him?

2. How did Julian make a kite?

3. What three things did Julian know about?

 4. What three wishes would you put in the tail of a kite?

Applying the Key Skill
Summarize

Read the sentences. Which sentence below has the same meaning? Write that sentence on your paper.

Julian wished that he could play soccer better than anyone. He also wished that he could fly in a plane.

a. Julian wished that he could play better soccer and go up in an airplane.

b. Julian wished that he could fly in a plane so that he would be better than anyone.

c. Julian wished that he could be better than anyone so he could play soccer and fly in an airplane.

I'm Up Here

I'm up here.
You're down there.
And nothing in that space between us
But a mile of air.
Where I sail:
Clouds pass.
Where you run:
Green grass.
Where I float:
Birds sing.
One thin thing there is
That holds us close together:
Kite string.

Karla Kuskin

A Kite of Your Own

Loretta Kaim

Gloria and Julian could tie a message to the tail of their kite. With these directions and a good wind, you will have a kite of your own. A friend may want to help just as Gloria helped Julian.

Have you watched a kite as it flew overhead? Did you wish that you had one, too? Well, you can have a kite of your own!

The price of a kite may be as little as $2.00. But you won't have to spend anything at all if you make your own kite. You can find most of the things you need to make a kite right in your home.

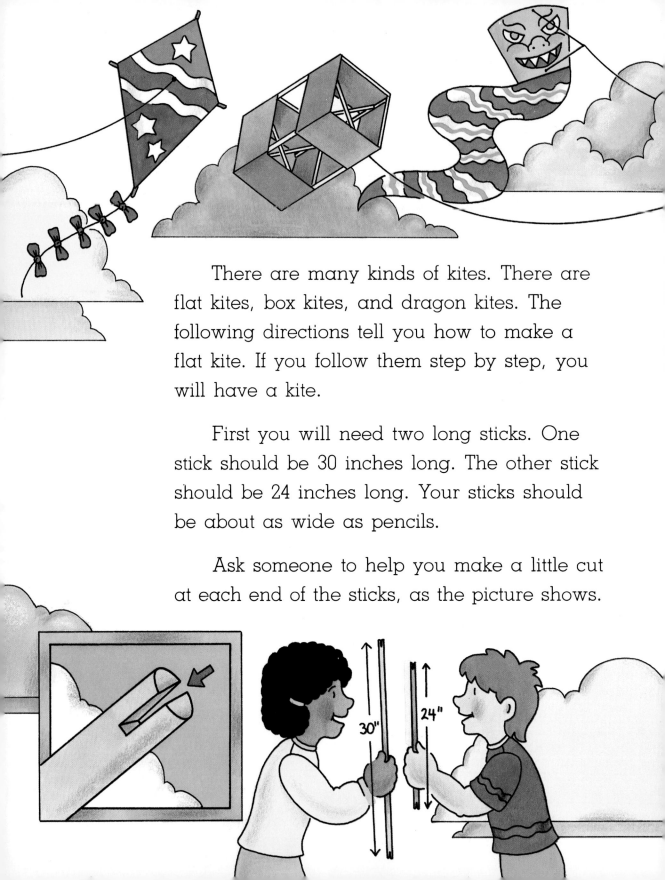

There are many kinds of kites. There are flat kites, box kites, and dragon kites. The following directions tell you how to make a flat kite. If you follow them step by step, you will have a kite.

First you will need two long sticks. One stick should be 30 inches long. The other stick should be 24 inches long. Your sticks should be about as wide as pencils.

Ask someone to help you make a little cut at each end of the sticks, as the picture shows.

Now take your long stick and draw a dot 8 inches from one end. Draw a dot 12 inches from one end of the other stick. Then put the sticks across each other to make a t. The sticks should cross at the dot. Wind a string around the place where the sticks cross and tie it. To make this tie even stronger, it should be covered with a coat of glue.

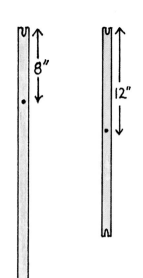

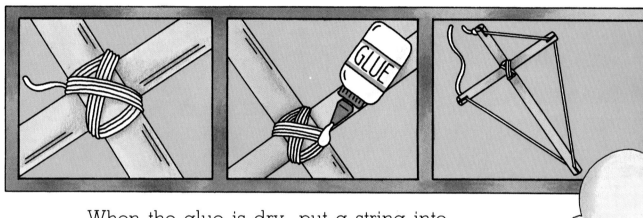

When the glue is dry, put a string into the top cut. Then run the string through the cut at the end of each stick. Place the string into each cut as you go along. Tie the string back at the top.

Now take some more string and wind it again around the end of each stick. This will help hold the first string in place. It will help keep your sticks from cracking, too.

Now it's time for your kite to be covered. Sometimes people use cloth, but most kites are covered with paper. If you use newspaper or a big bag, you won't have to spend anything for paper.

Put your paper on the floor and place the sticks on top of it. Hold the sticks in place with one hand. Trace around the string with the other. Then take the sticks off the paper. Do not cut on the trace, but cut 2 inches to the right of where you made the trace. Look at this picture before you cut. You will need to cut off each end of the paper, as the picture shows.

Now you can draw a picture on your kite. Draw a face, an animal, or anything at all. Make your picture big, so you can see it when your kite is flying overhead.

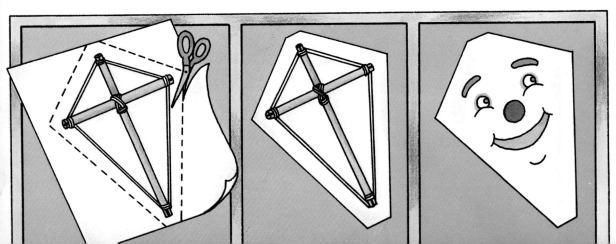

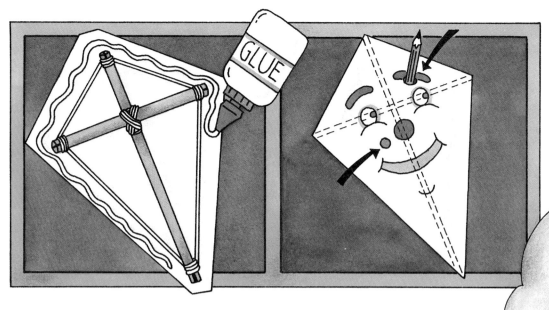

Now put your paper back on the floor with the picture down. Put the sticks on top of it. The stick that runs across should be on the top. Put a lot of glue on the outside 2 inches of the paper of your kite. Then push the paper onto the string. Push down hard to help the paper stay in place.

Wait for the glue to dry. Then make one dot to the right of where the sticks cross and another dot under it, as the picture shows. Push something little through the paper at each dot. (Pencils do a good job.) To make your kite stronger, glue a cloth or paper ring around each dot, on the front and the back of the kite.

Next you need a ball of string to fly your kite. Hold the kite so you can see your picture. Run the string through one ring, around the crossed sticks, and back out through the other ring. Then tie the string about 3 inches from the kite face.

Last of all, you need a tail. The job of the tail is to keep the kite from going sideways. If your kite does not have a tail it will spin all over the sky and quickly fall to the ground.

You can make a good tail from bits of
cloth about 2 inches wide and 6 inches long.
Tie these bits to a 13-foot long string. They
should be tied on the string every 6 inches or
so. After you have tied on as many bits of
cloth as you need, tie the string onto your
kite. Now your kite has a tail.

Now that you have learned how to make
a kite, you will need to make it fly somehow.
Have you watched as anyone flew a kite? If
not, here are some steps you can follow. As
you will soon see, it's not hard at all.

First, find a place where there are not
many trees. Trees can block the wind and get
in your way.

Put your back to the wind. Ask a helper
to take your kite about 25 feet away from you.

When a good wind comes along, tell
your helper to toss the kite up. At the same
time, you should walk back into the wind. As
the wind takes the kite up, let out more string
as quickly as you can. If you can get your
kite to stay up in the sky, you will know that
you have learned all about making a kite!

Thinking and Writing About the Selection

1. Name some things you will need to make a kite.

2. Where do you put the dots at the end of each stick?

3. How can you make your kite stronger?

 4. Write about how it would feel to see the wind take your kite for a ride in the sky.

Applying the Key Skill
Sequence of Events

The sentences below tell how to make a kite. Write the sentences in the correct order.

Then, put the sticks across each other to form a "t."

Next, glue the sticks together.

Last, tie a string and a tail to your kite.

First, you need to get two long sticks.

After that, cover your kite with paper.

WRITING activity

STORY

Prewrite

In "A Kite of Your Own," you read the directions for making a kite. You could make a kite of your own and even tie wishes into its tail as Julian and Gloria did. One of your wishes might be to take a trip. To your surprise, your wish comes true. Before you can say anything, you are as small as a bug and riding on the tail of your own kite. When you get home from your trip, you write a story about it for the newspapers.

Before you write, you need to make a plan for your story. Think about these questions. Your answers will help you plan what you will say in your story.

1. What places did you go to on your trip?
2. Where did you go first?
3. Where did you go next?
4. How or where did your trip end?
5. What can you tell about each place you saw on your trip?

Write

1. Use your plan to write your story.
2. Your first sentence should make people want to read your story. Try this one:

   I will never forget my high-flying ride on the tail of a kite.

3. Write sentences about the places you saw.
4. You may want to use Vocabulary Treasures in your story.
5. Write a title for your story.

Vocabulary Treasures	
floating	creaking
heavy	second

Revise

Read your story. Have a friend read it, too. Think about these things as you revise.

1. Do your sentences tell about the places you saw on your trip?
2. Could someone who reads your story tell one thing about each place? If not, what more can you say to help them?
3. Did you end each sentence with the right punctuation mark?
4. Now write your story again on another paper.

I Wish I Were Back Home

Argentina Palacios

You may feel sad to have to leave a friend.
But when you open your first letter from
a friend who is away, the message tells you
that your friend remembers you.

Delia and Alba were best friends. They lived next
door to each other in Patzcuaro, Mexico. When
Delia's father finds a new job at an aquarium in
New York City, Delia and her family will have to
move there for two years. She is sad to leave her
home and her grandpa and grandma. But, most of
all she is sad to leave Alba.

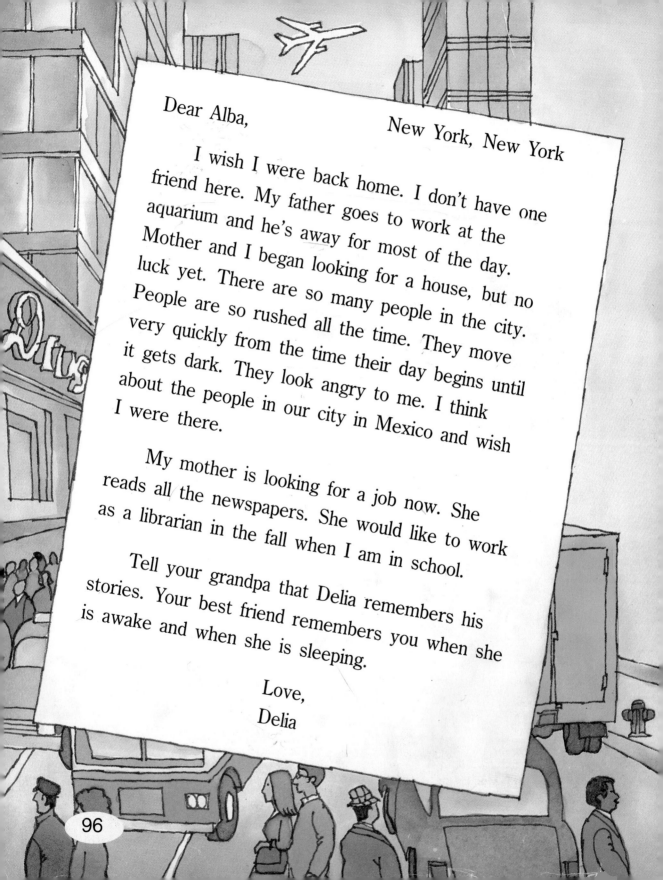

Dear Alba,   New York, New York

I wish I were back home. I don't have one friend here. My father goes to work at the aquarium and he's away for most of the day. Mother and I began looking for a house, but no luck yet. There are so many people in the city. People are so rushed all the time. They move very quickly from the time their day begins until it gets dark. They look angry to me. I think about the people in our city in Mexico and wish I were there.

My mother is looking for a job now. She reads all the newspapers. She would like to work as a librarian in the fall when I am in school.

Tell your grandpa that Delia remembers his stories. Your best friend remembers you when she is awake and when she is sleeping.

Love,
Delia

96

Patzcuaro, Mexico

Dear Delia,

I just got your letter. I hope my messages make you happy.

We all remember you, too. My grandpa and the rest of the family say "Hi" to you, your mother, and father.

Don't mind the angry looks on the people you see. They may not mean it. When you meet some friends you will feel better.

Have you gone to the aquarium with your dad yet? What did you see there? Give me your answers the next time you write.

We all went to play ball in the park the other day. Someone said, "I wish Delia were here." The rest of us said, "We miss Delia," which tells you how we feel with you away.

Love,
Alba

97

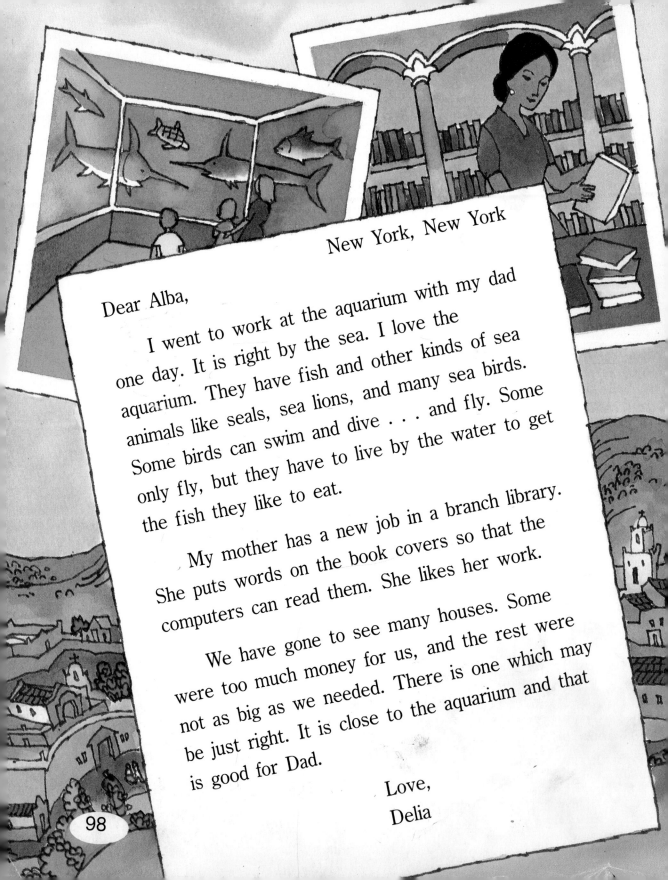

New York, New York

Dear Alba,

I went to work at the aquarium with my dad one day. It is right by the sea. I love the aquarium. They have fish and other kinds of sea animals like seals, sea lions, and many sea birds. Some birds can swim and dive . . . and fly. Some only fly, but they have to live by the water to get the fish they like to eat.

My mother has a new job in a branch library. She puts words on the book covers so that the computers can read them. She likes her work.

We have gone to see many houses. Some were too much money for us, and the rest were not as big as we needed. There is one which may be just right. It is close to the aquarium and that is good for Dad.

Love,
Delia

Dear Delia,   Patzcuaro, Mexico

When you said the aquarium is right by the sea, I thought of our city in Mexico, which is on a lake. Are you by a lake, too?

Do you know what you need before school begins and the days get dark before six o'clock? You need a trip to the zoo. That will make you happy, I know. There has to be a zoo in New York City.

Remember that your friend Alba answers when you write.

Love,
Alba

Dear Alba,   New York, New York

We went to the zoo, and what a zoo it was! We got there when it opened and stayed until it got dark and it was time to close. We had a peek in the elephant house. We saw them give the elephants a bath. I like to watch the elephants lean toward the water. One elephant pushes its head all the way under the water.

We saw many animals we knew and many we didn't know. There was a little zoo inside the big zoo. They had ducks, goats, and other animals to pet and feed. We heard a storyteller. She told a story about how the snake got its poison.

Our new house is a two-family house with a little yard but no trees.

School begins in two days. I think of it a lot. I wish I were back home, going to my own school, with all my friends.

Write back soon, please.

Your friend,
Delia

Dear Delia,

Patzcuaro, Mexico

I spoke with your grandma and grandpa after I got your letter. They said they got a letter from you, too. It is so much fun to get a letter from my friend Delia in New York City!

I am happy you went to the zoo. I would like to see that zoo some day, too.

Don't feel so bad. School begins soon and you will make a lot of friends. I hope you don't forget me then. Before you know it, you will be back home.

Love,

Alba

Thinking and Writing About the Selection

1. Why did Delia wish that she were back home?

2. Did Delia like the aquarium? Why?

3. How did this plan to write to each other help Delia and Alba?

4. What do you think Delia's first day at her new school will be like?

Applying the Key Skill
Final Consonant Clusters

Number your paper from 1 to 5. Then use the letters below to finish the words in each sentence. Write the words on your paper.

ft   sk   st   nk

1. Alba wants to get her friend a gi____.

2. First, she must thi____ of what to get.

3. Alba walks fa____ when she goes to the store.

4. At the store she looks at a so____ toy animal.

5. Then Alba sees a ma____ in the store.

Best Wishes, Ed

James Stevenson

Ed finds that he is all alone on an island of ice. Like Delia in "I Wish I Were Back Home," he begins to miss his friends. Messages help Ed find his way back home to his friends.

Ed lived on a big island of ice with Betty, Freddy, Al, and a lot of other penguins. Every day the penguins had fun as they tossed snowballs and ran across the ice. But they always watched out for Ernest, the big whale. Every time he went by . . . SPLAT! Ed and all the penguins got soaked.

"Watch what you are doing!" Betty would yell. But Ernest swam right by.

"Ernest doesn't even notice penguins," said Ed.

One night when Ed was asleep, he heard a loud noise, like ice cracking. Ed thought it was a dream.

When Ed woke up, he saw that the island of ice was cracking in two. He was all alone on an island of his own.

Ed's friends looked very little as his island floated away. Ed watched until he couldn't see them anymore.

Then he walked all over his island. There was nobody on it at all. At last he came to his own footprints again.

Some birds flew over. Ed waved, but they did not wave back. "I think I will be here the rest of my life," Ed said.

When the day was over, Ed wrote the words "I GIVE UP" in the snow. Then he went to sleep.

The next day a bird woke him up. "Hi," said the bird, "did you write that thing in the snow?"

"Yes," said Ed.

"Could you write something for me?" asked the bird.

"I think so," said Ed. "What do you want?"

"Tell my friends to meet me at the iceberg," said the bird. "Sign it *Talbot*. That is my name."

Talbot flew away, and Ed wrote the message.

MEET ME AT THE ICEBERG.

TALBOT

Pretty soon, Talbot's friends flew over and read the message. They waved to Ed, and Ed waved back.

All day long, birds came by and asked Ed to write messages for them. When the day was over, all of the island was covered with messages. Ed was very tired.

Talbot flew down and gave Ed a fish. "You are doing a very good job," said Talbot. "How come you look so sad?"

"I miss my friends on my other island," said Ed.

"Where is your other island?" asked Talbot.

"Way over there someplace," said Ed.

"Too bad you can't fly," said Talbot. "You could see it from the sky."

"Well, I can't fly," said Ed.

"It's not very hard," said Talbot.

"It is for penguins," said Ed. Talbot flew away.

"I think I will spend the rest of my life doing these messages," Ed said.

When Ed got up the next day, he saw a surprise.

ED—THERE'S A MESSAGE FOR YOU
FOLLOW THE SIGNS

He followed the signs until he came to another message.

SIT HERE AND WAIT →

He sat down on the X and waited. Suddenly there was a huge SPLAT! Ed was soaked. It was Ernest, the whale.

"I heard you are looking for a ride to that island with all the penguins on it," said Ernest.

"How did you know?" asked Ed.

"I heard it from Talbot," said Ernest. "Hop on my back."

"Wait one second," said Ed. "I have to leave a message."

Ed quickly wrote the message in the snow.

THANK YOU, TALBOT. BEST WISHES, Ed

Then he got on top of Ernest's back.

Ernest gave three quick splashes with his tail, and then they were flying across the water.

"Ed is back!" yelled Betty.

"At last!" shouted Freddy and Al.

Ed jumped off Ernest's back. "Thanks a lot, Ernest," shouted Ed.

"That's O.K.," said Ernest. "Just don't think you can have a ride every day."

"We are so glad you are back, Ed," said Betty.

"We missed you a lot," said Freddy and Al.

"I missed you," said Ed.

SPLAT! They were all soaked, as Ernest swam away.

"Oh," said Betty, "he did it again!"

"Ernest doesn't notice penguins," said Freddy.

"Sometimes he does," said Ed.

Thinking and Writing About the Selection

1. Who lived on the big island of ice?

2. What did Ed hear when he was asleep?

3. Why was Ed so tired at the end of the day?

4. Do you think that Talbot was a good friend? Why?

Applying the Key Skill
Initial Consonant Clusters

Use the letters below to finish the words in the paragraph. Write the paragraph on your paper.

     sw   sn   st

Ed ___ared at all the ___ow coming down. It had snowed for three days. Ed could not see in all that ___ow. He took a ___ep and fell into the water! Just then Ernest ___am by. "This is not a good day to ___im," he said, as he put Ed back on the ice.

REALISM AND FANTASY

Some things that happen in stories are real and some are make-believe. A penguin who writes messages is make-believe. But Delia and Alba were real girls who wrote real messages to each other. When you read, think about what is real and what is make-believe.

ACTIVITY A Look at the pictures. Then read the sentences. On your paper write the sentences that are make-believe.

1. The boy skated across the pond.
2. The bird had two braids.
3. The dragon floated in the sea.
4. The girl kicked the ball to the moon.
5. The kite is in a tree.
6. The whale swam for a long time.

ACTIVITY B Read the story. Write the answers to the questions on your paper. Use complete sentences.

A penguin lived in an aquarium with lots of other penguins and fish. He had food to eat and a spot to sleep. But he wanted to fly. One day he jumped into his plane, waved to his friends, and flew off on a trip to Puerto Rico.

1. Could a penguin live in an aquarium?
2. How is the penguin in this story like a real penguin?
3. Does the penguin in this story do anything that a real penguin would not do?

ALEXANDER CALDER:

"Just For the Fun of It"

Gail Tuchman

When Alexander Calder was a boy
he liked to look at the circus. He
made animals for people to see. The
circus had a message for Calder. He
put this message into his art.

Alexander Calder tells us many things through his art. In his work, we see his love of life. He liked to watch birds and bugs. He loved to see the red sun each day. He loved to see the moon smiling in the dark of night. Calder loved the circus and animals.

He would notice all the things around him. Each thing, big or little, touched him, and it would find its way into his art. Even now, Calder's art always feels like new— like a surprise.

From the age of eight, Calder began to make little play things. The kinds of play things he made as a child opened the door for the art that followed.

Anyone who knows Calder's work knows that a love of play is what Calder's art is about. Calder could turn a can into a bird, or wood into a chicken. He made bears that could skate and fish that could swim. Calder's work was like a picture that could move.

Chock. (1972). Whitney Museum of American Art.

Circus. (1926). Collection of Nanette Hayes Saxton.

"I want to make things that are fun to look at . . . ," said Calder. "I always loved the circus . . . so I [made] a circus just for the fun of it."

Calder's love for the circus began in the 1920s while he was doing art for magazines. He was asked to go to the Ringling Brothers Barnum and Bailey Circus.

Day after day and night after night, he watched things under the big top. He watched the lions, elephants, and seals do tricks. He watched people spring and turn cartwheels. Suddenly, overhead, someone would step out and walk across the big top as if she were a bird on a string. There was always a surprise.

Kangaroo, a figure from the *Circus.* (1926-31). Whitney Museum of American Art.

Calder would listen to all the circus sounds. He would listen to the calls of the seals and lions. He would listen to someone singing a song or playing a tune. Calder could tell by listening to the music what was going to happen next.

Then Calder made his own little art circus. He made animals and people from bits of cloth and wood and string. He gave his first circus shows on the floor in his room. Calder would turn on a light to show the circus ring. He put on records so that his friends could listen to "circus" music. Then the circus show began.

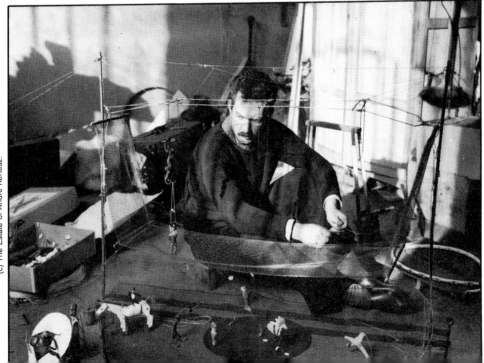

119

Calder sat on the floor next to the ring. He made the sounds for the seals and lions. He made all the animals and people move to the tune of the circus.

There was a dog that could sit up and even jump through a paper ring. Two seals tossed a ball again and again from one nose to another. There was a man who could pick up something heavy and hold it over his head. There was a woman singing tunes. There was someone who could spring onto the back of a pony.

When people watched Calder's circus, they had fun. Smiles bloomed on every face in the room. The people felt Calder's love of the circus.

Calder's work on paper showed his love of play. One learns that his painting has the feeling of his other work.

First, Calder would put the paper down flat. Next, he soaked it with water. He let the paper dry a little. Then, he began to paint. Sometimes Calder would use paint right from the can. He didn't always mix it. He would paint anything that came to mind. He gave each painting a life of its own. He covered a big sheet of paper with the sun, a face, or a bug.

Calder wanted his art to have life. He wanted his art to move. He makes you think of things in life that move. A little wind makes Calder's work move about. Fish swim. Birds fly. Flowers bloom. Leaves sail in the wind. It takes time to see all that follows.

As a boy, Calder would listen to the song of the wind. He would listen to the sounds of little birds. When one listens these sounds please the ears. It seems as though Calder wanted to please the eyes, as well, with things that move.

Seeing Calder's art makes you want to touch it. You want to move it a little with your fingers. It's as though you want to play, too— "just for the fun of it."

If your fingers could touch it, you would feel the love of life that lives in Calder's art.

Thinking and Writing About the Selection

1. Name some of the animals that Calder made.

2. What sounds would Calder listen to at the circus?

3. Do you think that people liked Calder's circus? Why?

 4. Which work of Calder's do you like best? Why do you like it?

Applying the Key Skill
Summarize

Read the two sentences. Choose the sentence below that has the same meaning. Write that sentence on your paper.

Alexander Calder liked to listen to the circus sounds. He could tell by listening to the songs what would happen next.

a. By listening to circus songs Calder could tell what would happen next.

b. Of all the sounds in the circus, Calder liked circus tunes the best.

Through Grandpa's Eyes

Patricia MacLachlan

Illustrated by Deborah Kogan Ray

Grandpa could not see Calder's circus. But Grandpa's eyes have a message for John. They tell him many things. John learns to see through Grandpa's eyes.

Of all the houses that I know, I like my grandpa's best. There are other fine houses. But Grandpa's house is the one I like most. Because I see it through Grandpa's eyes.

Grandpa is blind. He doesn't see the house the way I do. He sees in his own way. In the morning, the sun pushes through the shades into my eyes. I slide down under the covers to get away, but the light follows me. I give up, kick off the covers, and run to Grandpa's room.

The sun wakes Grandpa in another way. He says it touches him, warming him awake. When I peek in Grandpa's door, he is up. He smiles because he hears me.

"Good day, John."

"Where's Nana?" I ask him.

"Don't you know?" he says. "Close your eyes, John, and look through my eyes." I close my eyes and listen.

"Nana is making breakfast," I say. When I open my eyes, I see Grandpa looking at me.

Grandpa's eyes are sharp blue, even though they are not sharp seeing.

"Breakfast!" calls Nana. "I smell eggs and toast with jam," says Grandpa. He leans his head close to mine.

The wood railing on the steps shows a path where Grandpa has run his fingers up and down. I walk down the steps, too, my fingers following Grandpa's path.

We go in to eat breakfast. Nana hands us each a plate of food. As Grandpa begins to eat, his plate of food is a clock.

"Two eggs at nine o'clock and toast at two o'clock," says Nana to Grandpa.

"A drop of jam," I tell Grandpa, "at six o'clock."

I make my plate of food a clock, too, and eat through Grandpa's eyes.

After breakfast, I follow Grandpa's path to another room. He takes his cello.

"Will you play with me, John?" he asks.

"Listen," says Grandpa. "I will play a song I learned when I was your age. It was the song I liked best."

He plays the tune while I listen. That is the way Grandpa learns new tunes. By listening. "Now," says Grandpa, "the two of us can try it. That's fine," says Grandpa as we play.

Grandpa and I walk outside, to the front yard. We walk to the water. Grandpa was not blind all his life. He remembers in his mind the gleam of the sun on the water.

"I feel a south wind," says Grandpa.

I can tell which way the wind goes because I see the way the tops of the trees lean. Grandpa tells by the way the wind feels on his face.

When we come to the water, I see a blackbird with a red patch. It is on a cattail.

"What is that bird over there, Grandpa?"

"Conk-a-ree," the bird calls to us.

"A red-winged blackbird," says Grandpa.

He can't see where the bird is, but he hears the song of the bird.

As we walk back to the house, Grandpa stops suddenly. He leans his head and listens. He looks to the sky. "Honkers," he whispers.

I look up and see a flock of geese, flying in a V.

We walk up the path again and to the yard where Nana is painting some chairs. Grandpa smells the paint.

"What color, Nana?" he says. "I can't smell the color."

"Blue," I tell him. "Blue like the sky."

"Blue like the color of Grandpa's eyes," Nana says.

Late in the day, Grandpa, Nana, and I take some books outside to read under a tree. Grandpa reads his book with his fingers, feeling the Braille dots that tell him the words. As he reads, Grandpa laughs out loud.

"Tell us what the joke is," says Nana. "Read to us, Papa."

Grandpa does.

When dinner is over, Grandpa puts on the TV. I watch, but Grandpa listens. The sounds and the words tell him when something is happy or sad.

Somehow, Grandpa knows when it is dark, and he takes me up the steps and tucks me into bed. He leans down to kiss me, his hands feeling my head. "You need a haircut, John," he says.

Before Grandpa leaves, he tugs the light chain over my bed to turn off the light. He does not know it but he's put it on. I lie for a while until he's gone, before I get up to turn off the light.

Then, when it is dark for me the way it is dark for Grandpa, I hear the night sounds that Grandpa hears. The house creaking, the birds singing their last songs of the day, the wind playing with the trees outside.

Then, suddenly, I hear the sounds of geese overhead. They fly over the house.

"Grandpa," I whisper. I hope he's heard them, too.

"Honkers," he calls back.

"Go to sleep, John," says Nana.

Grandpa says her voice smiles to him.

"What?" I call to her.

"I said go to sleep," she answers.

She says it sternly. But Grandpa is right. Her voice smiles to me. I know. Because I am looking through Grandpa's eyes.

Thinking and Writing About the Selection

1. How does the sun wake up John?
2. How does the sun wake up Grandpa?
3. Why is Grandpa's plate of food a clock?
4. What other senses help Grandpa to "see"? How?

Applying the Key Skill
Sequence of Events

The sentences below tell what happened in the story "Through Grandpa's Eyes." Write the sentences in the right order.

Last, Grandpa and John walk outside to the water.

Then, Nana calls John and Grandpa to breakfast.

First, the sun wakes John and Grandpa up.

After breakfast, Grandpa plays the cello.

So Will I

My grandfather remembers long ago
the white Queen Anne's lace that grew wild.
He remembers the buttercups and goldenrod
from when he was a child.

He remembers long ago
the white snow falling falling.
He remembers the bluebird and thrush
at twilight
calling, calling.

He remembers long ago
the new moon in the summer sky.
He remembers the wind in the trees
and its long, rising sigh.
And so will I

      so will I.

Charlotte Zolotow

Many Messages

In these stories you read about finding a message in a secret code, a book, a letter, or the tail of a kite. But messages do not always have words—a smile has a special message, too. Messages help to bring friends closer together.

Thinking and Writing About *Many Messages*

1. How did Owl and Caterpillar help to change Bets' mind about reading? How did reading help Tim in "The Code Toad"?

2. In what stories did two people who didn't know each other at the beginning of the story make friends?

3. How did messages help the characters and animals in "Best Wishes, Ed" and "I Wish I Were Back Home"?

4. What might Grandpa in "Through Grandpa's Eyes" have remembered seeing before he was blind?

 5. Write a paragraph that tells why "Many Messages" is a good name for this unit.

136

Introducing Level 6

PENNIES AND PRESENTS

Everyone loves presents! If you learn to save, you could have money for something you want. In the stories in this unit, you will read about girls and boys who learn to save and earn money. You will also find out how some people spend their money. How could boys and girls earn and save some pennies, nickels, or dimes?

A penny saved is a penny earned.

137

A PENNY SAVED

Stephanie Calmenson

Money helps us buy things we need. And
sometimes you just want a little something
more. If you learn to put your money away,
you could have some money for what you
want. One of the best places to put money
is in a piggy bank. Amy and Scott learn
how they can get what they want and where
they can keep their money.

Amy listened to the tunes that played on her grandpa's pine music box.

"You can get one just like it," said her grandpa, "if you can save a little money each day. Soon you will have as much as you need."

Amy thought for a time, looking at the box, and said, "That's what I'll do! I'll save for it."

That afternoon, Amy and Scott were at the library looking through a book about banks with their grandpa.

"A penny saved is a penny earned," their grandpa read. "That is what Ben Franklin said about two hundred years back. It says in this book that the first penny in America was made in 1793 and the first penny bank was made around the same time."

Amy and Scott looked at each picture. There were many banks to admire. Amy liked the China Pig best.

"Would you read what it says about this piggy bank, Grandpa?" Amy asked.

"It says that this kind of bank was sold in the 1890s and 1900s for as little as ten cents. The bank did not open, so you had to shake it if you wanted to get your money out."

"That sounds like a lot of work," said Amy.

"Yes," said her grandpa. "It was so hard to get the money out that sometimes people just left their money in. When money is in the bank, people can't spend it. So this bank helped people save their money."

"I like these," said Scott.

"They are called mechanical banks," said Grandpa. "The first one of its kind was made in China. The first one in America was made in the late 1860s."

"Here is an Uncle Sam bank," said Amy. "How does it work?"

"Uncle Sam puts the penny into his bag," said Grandpa. "And look at this Mother Eagle bank. The penny goes from the mother to the baby."

"How does this dog bank work?" asked Scott.

"You put the penny on the nose of the dog, then tug his tail," said Grandpa. "His head goes back, and the penny drops in."

"That's neat!" shouted Amy and Scott.

"You are in the library," whispered Grandpa. "We have to be quiet here."

"All right," whispered Scott, as he looked at another bank that showed three ball players. "Would you tell us about this bank Grandpa?"

Scott's grandpa read from the book, "This is called the Calamity bank. When a penny is dropped into the bank, a player will turn to run. But the other two players also turn and stop him."

"If I had a bank like one of these, I would save so many dollars," said Scott.

"How many would you save?" asked Amy.

"I expect I would save about ten or twenty dollars," said Scott.

"Well, I would save fifty or a hundred dollars!" said Amy.

"Would the two of you like to try to save some money in a bank?" Grandpa asked.

"We certainly would," said Scott.

143

"Come, then," said Grandpa. "We will see if we can buy a bank for each of you. Then you can start to save your money."

Outside, they looked in window after window. At last they saw the right place.

"I would like to buy one bank for Scott and one for Amy," said Grandpa. "Will you show us where they are?"

"Certainly," said the man. "There are some in the window, and we have some more back here. Come and see if there are any that you like."

Amy, Scott, and Grandpa went to look. There were so many to admire. One had a tag that said, "Sold" on it. It was a beautiful China Pig.

"I wish this one were not sold so we could buy it," Amy said.

"I sold that one right before you came in, but I have one I think you will like just as much. I will be right back," said the man.

While he was gone, Scott saw the bank he wanted.

"This one has a place to put each penny, nickel, dime, and quarter," said Scott. "And this bank can tell how much money I have put in. When I have saved ten dollars, the bank will open."

"That certainly is a fine bank," said Grandpa.

Just then the man came back with a piggy bank for Amy. It was a beautiful one. Amy had to admire it.

145

"Thank you," she said. "I didn't expect it to be as beautiful as the other, but I like this one even better."

Grandpa asked the man how much each bank cost and gave him the money. The man gave him twenty cents in change.

Grandpa gave Amy and Scott ten cents each. "Now you can start to save your money," he said.

"Thank you, Grandpa," they said. "We are going to start to save our money right now. As Ben Franklin said, 'A penny saved is a penny earned.'"

Thinking and Writing About the Selection

1. This story tells us two things that were made around 1793. What were they?

2. Do you think it is good to have a piggy bank that does not open? Why?

3. How can you tell from the story that Scott and Amy would like to save money?

 4. Which bank would you have picked? Why?

Applying the Key Skill
Number of Syllables

Number your paper from 1 to 4. Read the words in each row. Write the words that have only one syllable on your paper.

1. cent   penny   spend   quarter
2. pine   money   dollar   shake
3. picture   pig   save   admire
4. grandpa   bank   nickel   change

Money's Funny

Money's funny
Don't you think?
Nickel's bigger than a dime;
So's a cent;
But when they're spent,
Dime is worth more
Every time.

Money's funny.

Mary Ann Hoberman

FLAGS FOR SALE

Franz Brandenberg

Illustrations by Aliki Brandenberg

Amy and Scott saved their money in "A Penny Saved." But if you have not saved your money, you may want to learn about Leo and Emily's idea to make money.

"I wish we had a flag for our shed," said Emily.

"I saw an advertisement for flags in one of the newspapers," said Leo. "A hundred cost ten dollars."

"We don't need a hundred," said Emily. "We need only one."

"We could sell the other ninety-nine," said Leo.

"At a profit," said Emily. "That's a good idea."

"If a hundred cost ten dollars," said Leo, "then one costs only ten cents."

"We can sell them for twenty cents each," said Emily.

"Then we will make a profit of ten cents on each flag," said Leo.

"Nine dollars and ninety cents for ninety-nine," said Emily.

"That's a lot of money," said Leo.

"Let's order them," said Emily.

You're a mathematical genius, Ms. Einstein.

"Do you have any money?" asked Leo.

"No," said Emily.

"Neither do I," said Leo.

"How can we buy them then?" asked Emily.

"We could borrow from our parents," said Leo. "And pay them back when we have sold the flags."

"That's a good idea," said Emily.

"I have never heard of a flag that costs only ten cents," said Emily's mother.

"That's the wholesale price," said Emily.

"All right, I'll lend you five dollars," said her mother.

"My mother didn't believe that they cost only ten cents," said Leo.

"Neither did mine," said Emily.

"But she did lend me five dollars," said Leo.

"So did mine," said Emily.

A week later a package came in the mail.

"Can I open it, please?" asked Emily.

"Let's open it together," said Leo.

"They are very small flags," said Emily. "And made of paper!"

"What did you expect for ten cents?" asked Leo.

"They are not the kind you put on a shed," said Emily. "They are the kind you stick on birthday cakes."

"A small flag on the shed is better than none," said Leo.

They look like three-cent flags to me

"Let's start with the selling," said Emily.

They sold the flags to many, many people. When they were finished selling, they still had fifty left.

"I think we overbought," said Emily. "We only sold fifty."

"We made ten dollars," said Leo.

"That's what we got from our parents," said Emily. "We didn't make any profit."

"But we have fifty flags left over that didn't cost us anything!" said Leo.

"What are we going to do with fifty flags?" asked Emily.

"Fifty flags on the shed are better than one," said Leo.

"We have such good ideas!" said Emily.

154

Thinking and Writing About the Selection

1. How much did a hundred flags cost? How much was one flag?

2. If Emily and Leo only needed one flag, why would they buy one hundred flags?

3. Emily and Leo borrowed the money they needed from their parents. How can children make their own money?

4. What do you think of Emily and Leo's "good idea"?

Applying the Key Skill
Main Idea

Read the story. Then answer the question. Write the correct answer on your paper.

Leo and Emily want to save money. They would like to buy a rug for their shed. Leo thinks they could save money if they had a piggy bank.

What is the main idea?

a. Leo and Emily need to buy a piggy bank.

b. Leo and Emily want to save money.

c. Leo and Emily want to buy a rug.

PREDICT OUTCOMES

You already know much about people, animals, places, and things. Using what you already know together with the information you get from a story will help you to predict what will happen next. When you read, think about what you know and try to predict what will happen in a story.

ACTIVITY Read each story. Then write the answer to the questions on your paper.

1. Jill was working on a painting for the art show. She began to paint a picture of the sun setting. She put a flock of geese in the blue sky. She put red-winged blackbirds on long cattails. It was beautiful.

What do you think will happen next?
   Jill will bring her painting to the art show.
   Jill will give her painting to her mother.
   Jill will start over on the painting.

2. Dan wanted to learn to play the cello. He went to school. He talked to the music teacher. She let Dan try the cello. He liked the sounds the cello made.

What do you think will happen next?
Dan will learn how to sing.
Dan will learn how to play the cello.
Dan will play records.

3. Carlos needed some information for his report. He went to the library. He read books, newspapers, and magazines. He talked to the librarian. He wrote some ideas on his paper.

What do you think will happen next?
Carlos will call a friend.
Carlos will go to the library.
Carlos will begin to write his report.

4. Emily really wanted a new piggy bank for her collection. She sold some little flags. She took care of the little boy next door. She cut the grass. She saved the money that she had earned.

What do you think will happen next?
Emily will buy more flags.
Emily will walk in the grass.
Emily will buy a new piggy bank.

My Train

by Judith Nayer

In the story "Flags for Sale" Emily and Leo wanted flags for their shed. Have you ever seen something that you admire and want to have for your very own? In this story you will read about a girl who has a very special collection.

Collection

Have you ever loved something from the second you saw it? That's what happened to me when I saw a train set for the first time. I was only six. My dad bought a train set for my brother.

To the surprise of my whole family, I was the one who wanted to play with it. I thought that train set was really special. I sat there just watching it for a long time. I would count each time the train went around the track.

Right after that my dad bought me a train set. It had a grand old steam engine. It had four different cars. One was a coach car. That was where the people would sit. The last car was the caboose. That was where the people who worked on the train would eat and sleep. To me it was the finest train set ever made. I guess that's because it was my first, and my very own.

Now I have a whole collection of trains.
Some have a steam engine, like the old train
my dad bought me. The rest have a diesel
engine. Most trains run on diesel. The steam
engine is not in use anymore because it isn't
as clean or as quick as the diesel.

I've bought most of the trains myself. If a
train I wanted to buy cost too much, I would
save my money and buy it when it went on
sale. Another way to save money is to buy
train kits. Kits don't cost as much because you
have to put the trains together on your own.
It can be hard, but it's fun, too. I love to paint
the cars different colors.

There are train magazines that can help someone who has a train collection to buy more trains. If someone wants a special train they can put an advertisement in the train magazines. Someone else who may have that train will read the advertisement. This way people can buy and sell trains.

Last week I went to a train show. I met so many people there! Some people were selling trains and other people were showing their trains.

There were many more trains than I've ever seen. It would have been hard to count them, but there must have been more than a hundred different kinds of trains. Some were really grand. The closer you got to them, the more you saw how special they were.

I'm really glad to know other people who like trains as much as I do. It hasn't been as hard to find trains for my collection. And it's good to know that someone else may have just the train I need.

I'm certainly going to keep up with my collection. Who knows? You may see my train set at a show one day.

Thinking and Writing About the Selection

1. What kind of engine did the girl in this story have first?

2. Why is a caboose needed on a train?

3. How can you save money when you buy trains?

 4. Write about a collection that you would like to have.

Applying the Key Skill
Interpret Graphic Aids

Read the chart. Then answer the questions on your paper.

Train Parts			
	Cabooses	Engine	Boxcars
Leo	1	1	5
Clara	2	3	4

1. How many cabooses does Leo have?

2. How many boxcars does Clara have?

3. Who has more than one engine?

The Best Train Set Ever

Everyone knows that a
birthday present can cost money.
Now you can read about a family that
gets together to buy a train set for a
birthday present. How will they surprise
each other and Peter?

Pat Hutchins

There was a train set in Mindy's window. Every morning on his way to school Peter stopped to admire it.

"That sure is the finest train set I've ever seen," he would say. "Just look at that engine, that coach, that flat truck, that caboose, and that track. A fine train set like that must cost a lot of money."

"Come on," said his brothers and sisters. "We'll be late for school."

"What are you getting Peter for his birthday?" Anna asked Ma and Pa. "He sure wants that train set in Mindy's window!"

"We are not telling," said Ma. "No one can keep a secret in this family."

"We have got ten dollars to spend," said Pa. "Let's go and see what the train set costs."

"How much is that train set in the window?" Ma asked.

"Thirty dollars," said Mr. Mindy.

"Too bad." Ma sighed. "We were hoping it would be closer to ten."

"The engine costs ten dollars," said Mr. Mindy. "It's a grand engine!"

"It sure is," Pa agreed, "but not much use on its own."

Ma picked up the engine. "Well," she said, "it would be a start."

"What are you getting Peter for his birthday?" Anna asked Tony. "He sure wants that train set."

"I'm not telling," said Tony. "No one can keep a secret in this family."

I've saved eight dollars from helping at the drugstore, thought Tony. I will go and see what the train set costs.

"How much is the train set in the window?" Tony asked.

"Thirty dollars for the set," said Mr. Mindy, "but we just sold the engine."

"Oh!" said Tony. "I was hoping it would be around eight."

"The track costs eight dollars," said Mr. Mindy. "It's the best kind of track."

"It certainly is the best kind of track," Tony agreed, "but not much use on its own."

"It's a start," said Mr. Mindy.

"What are you giving Peter for his birthday?" Frank asked Anna. "He really wants that train set."

"I'm not telling," said Anna. "No one can keep a secret in this family."

I've saved five dollars from running errands, thought Anna. I'll go and see what it costs.

"How much is the train set in the window?" Anna asked.

"Thirty dollars for the set," said Mr. Mindy, "but I just sold the engine and the track."

"I've only got five dollars," said Anna.

"The coach is five," said Mr. Mindy. "It's a beautiful coach."

"It's a beautiful coach all right," Anna agreed. "And I guess it's a start!"

"What are you giving Peter for his birthday?" Maria asked Frank.

"I'm not telling," said Frank. "No one can keep a secret in this family."

I've got four dollars saved, thought Frank. I'll go and see what that train set costs.

"What happened to that train in the window?" Frank asked. "I've got four dollars and I wanted to buy it."

"I've just sold the engine, the track and the coach," said Mr. Mindy, "but the caboose is four dollars."

"It's a very fine caboose," said Frank, "but not much use on its own."

"It's a start," said Mr. Mindy.

Maria had three dollars saved. I'll go and see what that train set costs, she thought.

"How much is that train set you had in the window?" she asked.

"Thirty dollars for the set," said Mr. Mindy, "but I've just sold the engine, the track, the coach, and the caboose. The flat car is all that is left. But that is three dollars."

"Well," said Maria, "a flat car's not much use on its own, but I'll take it."

The next day Peter woke up first, before everyone else. Everyone else was still asleep. I'll just go and look at the train, he thought, before everyone gets up. When he got there the train was gone.

"Too bad." Peter sighed, and walked slowly home.

"What's wrong?" asked Ma as Peter opened the door. "It's your birthday and you look so sad."

"I've just been to Mindy's," said Peter, "and the train set's gone."

"Is it?" said Ma and Pa. "Well, here's the engine. Happy birthday!"

"Gosh!" said Tony. "I've bought you the track!"

"I bought you the coach!" cried Anna.

"I bought you the caboose!" shouted Frank.

"How about that!" screamed Maria. "I bought you the flat car!"

"I told you!" said Ma, as Peter stared at the parcels. "No one can keep a secret in this family. He hasn't even opened them yet!"

But he soon did, and it certainly was the finest train set Peter had ever seen.

Thinking and Writing About the Selection

1. What parts of the train set did Peter admire?

2. How did Tony save eight dollars?

3. Why did Peter look sad on his birthday?

4. Do you think it is true that no one in this family could keep a secret?

Applying the Key Skill
Predict Outcomes

Use complete sentences to answer the questions about Peter in "The Best Train Set Ever."

1. How did you know why Peter was sad on the morning of his birthday?

2. When Peter saw the train set, what do you think he did?

3. Do you think Peter will want to add other cars to his set? Why or why not?

Pat Hutchins

"I feel books for children should be logical—and most of all—fun; and that a good children's book should be enjoyed by adults, too."

There were seven children in Pat Hutchins' family, as well as a dog, a cat, white mice, and a crow. "To escape from the noise," she recalls, "Sooty the crow and I would set off across the fields, and while he looked for grubs and worms, I sketched."

Pat likes her stories to make sense. "I like to build my stories up so the reader can understand what is happening."

Pat's husband has worked with her to illustrate many of her books.

More to Read *1 Hunter, The Tale of Thomas Mead, Don't Forget the Bacon*

TAKE A RIDE

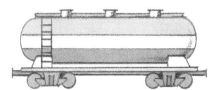

tank car

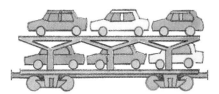

rack car

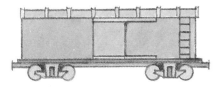

boxcar

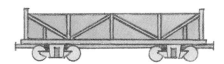

flat car

A boxcar looks like a box. That is how it got its name. How do you think each of the other cars got their names?

Here are other names of things people ride in. How do you think each word got its name?

subway   spaceship
airplane   seaplane

175

Surprises

Surprises are round
   Or long and tallish.
Surprises are square
   Or flat and smallish.

Surprises are wrapped
   With paper and bow,
And hidden in closets
   Where secrets won't show.

Surprises are often
   Good things to eat;
A get-well toy or
   A birthday treat.

Surprises come
   In such interesting sizes—
I LIKE
   SURPRISES!

Jean Conder Soule

Bit by Bit

Lisa Yount

Rosa's family, like Peter's family in "The Best Train Set Ever," helps her get what she wants most. But Rosa doesn't have a birthday surprise. She works hard for what she wants—and learns a way to save money.

"I would like to get a computer," said Rosa Hernández one morning.

Ramón, Rosa's brother, laughed at her. "What do you know about computers?" he said.

"I've used a computer in school," Rosa told him. "I know they can do many things. They can make lists and they can add numbers."

"We can't buy you a computer," said Rosa's father. "They cost a lot of money."

"Some don't," said Rosa. She showed her father an advertisement in one of the newspapers.

"That's still more than we can give you," Rosa's mother said.

"I know. I'll try and earn the money myself," Rosa said. "This summer I'll work for people in the neighborhood. I'll save the money I earn and buy a computer. My teacher says computers break everything we tell them into little parts called bits. That's how I'll get money for my computer—bit by bit."

"I'll help you," said Ramón. "I can give you some of the money I earn from my paper route."

"We can help, too," said Rosa's mother and father. "We will match the amount of money you earn each week. If you make five dollars, we will give you five dollars. Then you will have ten dollars."

"I'll get started right now!" said Rosa.

The next day Rosa and Ramón went to the park. "Sometimes people leave bottles here," Ramón said. "The market will give us money for bringing them back. I'll show you which kind. We can get a dime for the little bottles and two dimes for the big bottles."

Ramón and Rosa picked up three little bottles and one big one. They put them in Rosa's wagon.

On their way home, Ramón and Rosa met their neighbor Mrs. Yee.

"That's a big wagon," Mrs. Yee said. "It looks like it holds a lot."

"Yes," Rosa said. "We use it to carry bottles. We are going to get money for them. We are saving to buy a computer."

"I'll give you money, too, if you will help me," said Mrs. Yee. "It's hard for me to carry all my things from the market. If you bring your wagon and carry the things I buy home, I'll give you two dollars every week."

"Thank you, Mrs. Yee," cried Rosa.

A week later, Rosa went to the bank. She had two dollars from Mrs. Yee. She had $1.10 from bottles she had picked up that week. She had earned $3.10, so she got $3.10 from her mother and father. Ramón had given her $3.00 from his paper route.

"I would like to put my money in the bank," Rosa told the woman at the bank.

The woman gave Rosa a savings book. It showed how much money she put in the bank.

"If you leave your money here a while, you will earn more money," the woman told her. "We give you money while the bank makes use of your money. That kind of money is called interest. The interest will be only a little bit at first. But it can grow."

Rosa asked other people in her neighborhood what work she could do for them.

"Mrs. Long and I are going away for a week," Mr. Long said. "We need someone to watch our bird. We'll pay you fifty cents a day to do that."

For the rest of the summer, Rosa watched some pets for her neighbors. Each time Rosa earned money for her work, she put it in the bank. The list of numbers in her bank book got longer and longer.

At last it was the week before school. Rosa got her money out of the bank. It was a surprise for Rosa to see how much she had made, but she still didn't have quite as much as she needed.

"Let's go look at some computers, anyway," Rosa said to the family. "At least we can look at the computer I want." So off they all went.

But the computer store had a surprise for Rosa. The computer she wanted was on sale that week!

The woman counted Rosa's money. "You have more than you need for this computer," she said.

"I earned it," Rosa said smiling, "bit by bit."

Thinking and Writing About the Selection

1. Did Rosa's father think that she could buy a computer?

2. How did Rosa and Ramón use their wagon to earn money?

3. How much money did Rosa put in the bank after one week?

4. What helped the list of numbers in Rosa's bank book to get longer and longer?

Applying the Key Skill
Plot and Setting

Read the story. Then answer each question in a complete sentence.

Rosa went to the computer store. She wanted to buy a small computer. A woman showed Rosa many different kinds of computers. Then she found one that was on sale. Rosa had even more money than she needed.

1. Where does the story take place? Draw a picture that shows the setting.

2. What happens at the computer store?

PLOT AND SETTING

Every story has a plan. The plot is the author's plan for the things that will take place in a story. The plot can be about buying a computer or selling flags.

The setting of a story is where the story takes place. The setting can be in a home or on an island of ice. There may be many settings in a story.

ACTIVITY Read the paragraph. Think about the setting and the plot. Then write answers to the questions on your paper. Use complete sentences.

Alex lived on a small island. Every day, Alex watched as boats would sail across the water to the big city. Alex wanted to sail on one of those boats.

He wanted to take a trip to the big city.
So Alex began to save his money. He
did errands for people on the island,
and soon he had enough for his trip.
Then Alex wrote a letter to his friend
Peter who lived in the big city. He
told Peter to expect him in one week.
Alex couldn't wait for the day that
he would sail away to the big
city and be with his friend.

1. Where does the story take place?
2. What did Alex want to do?
3. How did Alex earn money?
4. Why did Alex write a letter to Peter?
5. What do you think Alex and Peter will
   do in the big city?

Amanda's Computer Kingdom

Gibbs Davis

In "Bit by Bit," Rosa saved some money to buy a computer. In the story you are about to read, Amanda learns that her family's computer is not only for business. It can do some very special things.

Amanda listened to a small voice coming from the radio. "Snow is now four feet deep. Every school in the city is closed. Records show that this is the coldest day in years."

Amanda blew into her hands and rubbed them together. She felt colder just listening to the snow report.

Amanda looked around the empty room. Her parents were at work. Amanda was spending the day at home with her brother, but he was in the next room reading a library book.

She remembered her school report. She was way behind, but she couldn't help it. She couldn't think of one thing to write about. She wished her teacher allowed everyone to draw a report. Amanda loved to draw. Art was one of the few things she was especially good at.

Amanda went into her parents' room and sat down behind the computer. Sometimes Amanda's mother let her write letters on it. Her mother did business on it. Amanda wasn't allowed to use the computer when her parents were not at home, but there was nothing else to do. Anyway, school work was business.

"Just this one last time," thought Amanda. She pushed *ON* and listened to the hum of the computer. She began her report:

My school report is about . . .

Her mind was empty. Amanda started over.

What my report is about is . . .

It was no use. Last week Amanda's mother showed her how to draw with the computer. Amanda knew just what to push to make a line. Add a few dots and a line turns into a belt. Amanda began to piece together a small picture on the computer. It was tricky, but she was getting good at it. Add another line and the belt turns into a bridge that goes across a small pond. She began to draw a path which led to a castle with a gold door.

When Amanda was finished, there before her was a beautiful magic kingdom.

To her surprise, steam floated out from under the gold door. Suddenly, the door opened. Steam covered everything! Amanda rubbed her eyes. She couldn't see a thing.

"It feels as if I am floating . . . floating down through the steam," thought Amanda.

Amanda felt as if a bird had dropped her from the sky. She didn't know what to do, so she just closed her eyes, hoping she would touch down in one piece.

As Amanda's feet touched the ground, she heard a gruff voice from behind her.

"Look what dropped in for dinner, Queenie. A troll."

When Amanda looked around to see where the voice was coming from, she couldn't believe her eyes.

Behind Amanda sat a king and queen in a castle almost like the one she had made on her mother's computer. If Amanda didn't know any better she would have thought she fell right through the computer into her own picture!

192

"Where am I?" asked Amanda.

"Don't you know where you are?" asked the king.

"No," answered Amanda. She rubbed her hands together.

"She doesn't know much for a troll," said the king.

"I'm not a troll," said Amanda.

"Then why are you so small?" said the queen, sternly. As the queen came closer, Amanda saw that her belt was a sleeping squirrel!

"I'm a child," said Amanda.

"You can't be a child," said the queen. "They are not allowed in this kingdom. If you are not a troll, that means you must be a flower." She rang for a messenger. "Water this flower so she will grow," said the queen.

Before Amanda could say anything, the messenger had opened a few bottles of water over Amanda's head. When they were empty, the messenger ran to get a few more.

"Wait!" yelled Amanda. "I'm not a flower! I'm a child!"

"How long does it take for a child to grow?" asked the king.

"Years," said Amanda.

"How sad," said the queen and sat down to eat. "Have some soup, my dear. It will make you feel much better. My turtle soup is especially good stuff. It is the coldest soup in the kingdom."

"Coldest?" said Amanda. Almost nothing made sense here. As Amanda took her place for dinner, she couldn't help but notice Queenie's necklace. It was a chain of especially small turtles.

"Dive in," said the queen. Just then, one of the turtles in Queenie's necklace made a back dive right into her soup!

"I admire a good diver, don't you?" asked the queen. "Back dives can be so tricky."

"Yes, very tricky," agreed Amanda, watching the turtle swim around. The turtle looked up at Amanda and waved.

Suddenly the king jumped up. "I know just the game to play after dinner!"

"Hold your tongue!" said the queen. The king quickly took hold of his tongue with his fingers.

Amanda couldn't help laughing. She whispered to the king, "I think she means for you to be quiet."

"No, I didn't," said the queen. "Don't people say what they mean where you live?"

"Not really," said Amanda. She began to think she would never get home again.

"Tell us about your kingdom," he said.

"I'll show you," said Amanda. She took out a clean piece of paper and began to draw her house. When she was almost finished, one of Queenie's turtles took a dive into Amanda's soup. Big splashes of soup fell onto her picture.

"Quick!" shouted the queen. "A cloth!"

As Amanda rubbed the picture dry, steam slowly began floating up from it until she couldn't see the king or the queen or even the turtles.

As Amanda felt her feet leave the ground, she crossed her fingers. Then, Amanda heard the hum of a computer and opened her eyes—she was back home!

Suddenly she heard the front door close. Her parents were home from work! Amanda quickly pushed *OFF*. The computer kingdom was gone.

"Hi, dear." Amanda's mother came into her room. "Get any ideas for your report?"

"Nothing much," said Amanda. Her mother would never believe it, anyway.

Then, Amanda got out a piece of paper and wrote THE COMPUTER KINGDOM in big letters. She had so much to say that she didn't know where to start.

Thinking and Writing About the Selection

1. Why was school closed on this day in the city?

2. What made Amanda think that she could use the computer?

3. What was Amanda doing before she felt her feet leave the ground to go back home?

4. What do you think Amanda will write about in her report?

Applying the Key Skill
Initial Consonants

Use the letters below to finish the words. Write the paragraph on your paper.

ph   kn   wh   wr

"__o is it?" Amanda asked. "I don't __ow," her mother said as she answered the __one, "but the woman is asking for you." The woman told Amanda she had won a computer because she __ote the best story about computers for a magazine.

WRITING activity

ADVERTISEMENT

Prewrite

Amanda, in "Amanda's Computer Kingdom," liked to use the computer. In "Bit by Bit," Rosa wanted a computer, too. Like Rosa, if you wanted a computer, you could work hard and save your money. One way you could earn money is to sell something. You might make something like kites to sell. You might even sell a toy such as a truck or a doll you don't play with anymore. You can write an advertisement for radio, TV, or newspapers that will help you make a sale.

First, think about what you will sell. Before you write, plan what you will say. You must put this information in your advertisement:

1. The name of what you want to sell
2. What it looks like
3. How much money you want for it
4. Your name and telephone number

An advertisement has to get people's interest. What words can you use to do that?

Write

1. Your first sentence should tell what you are selling. Try to use words that will interest people in reading your advertisement such as:

   A beautiful doll wants a new home!

2. Now write the rest of your sentences.
3. You may want to use Vocabulary Treasures in your advertisement.

Vocabulary Treasures	
costs	admire
special	finest

Revise

Read your advertisement. Have a friend read it, too. Think about these things as you read.

1. Look at the plan you made. Did you give all the needed information? If not, what should you add?
2. Did your advertisement get your friend's interest? If not, look for some other words that will.
3. Did you use a capital letter in the first word of each sentence?
4. Now write your advertisement again on another paper.

LET'S GO

Loretta Kaim

When you have money and need to buy food, you might use a special store called a supermarket. Read to find out some things you may not know about supermarkets.

SHOPPING

Did you ever think about all the things that go on inside a supermarket? Did you know that a supermarket is really just two huge rooms? The front room has rows and rows of shelves filled with all kinds of things for people to buy. People do their shopping in this room.

But a truck that is carrying things for the supermarket to sell would not bring the boxes right into this front room. The boxes would first go into a huge back room.

Each box will stay in the back room until the things in it are needed on the supermarket shelves. Then a grocery clerk will put the box on a big cart and push it into the front room.

The clerk must be sure to find the right row for each thing. One row may have bottles of things to drink. Another row may have all of the different kinds of cereal.

203

When the clerk has found the right row, he or she will put the things up on the shelves. But before anything can go up on the shelves, it must be given a price. The price shows how much the supermarket will charge you.

Now let's plan a shopping trip. It's usually a good idea to think about what you need before you get to the supermarket. You should write out a shopping list showing each of the things you have decided to buy. Without a list, it would be easy to forget something. But with a list, you will be sure to remember everything.

You may want to look in the newspaper before you go shopping. The newspaper will show you what things are on sale. You might even find a coupon for something you need. A coupon can save you money. Sometimes you can even get something for free with a coupon.

Now that you have made your list and looked in the newspaper, you are ready to go to the supermarket.

A supermarket usually has two doors. You should use the one that says "IN" when you are going in. You will use the one that says "OUT" when you come back out. Both of these doors will open and close as if by magic.

If you are going to buy a lot of things, you will need to use a shopping cart. You can put everything that you want to buy into your cart. At first your cart will be empty, but soon it will be filled both with things to eat and with other things like trash bags and magazines.

Even though a supermarket is a very big and noisy place, it will be easy for you to find what you need. Each row has just a few kinds of things in it, and there's usually a sign that tells what is in the row. If you can't find something, you can always ask a clerk to help you.

As you go up and down the rows, remember to look at your list. If you don't, you may bring home apples and peanut butter, when you really need eggs and milk!

You should always look at the prices as you shop. You may want to buy a brand that is on sale or the brand that you have a coupon for. If you buy a bigger package of something, you may save some money.

When you have filled your cart with what you have decided to buy, you are ready to go to the check-out counter. Be sure to look at your list one last time to make sure you have not missed anything!

When you get to the check-out counter, take everything that you have decided to buy out of your cart and put it up on the counter. If you have a coupon for something that you bought, you must put it up on the counter, too.

The check-out clerk will charge you for the things that you bought. Then he or she will give you a long piece of paper that shows the cost of each thing and tells you how much your bill is.

After you have given the clerk the right amount of money, your things will be put into bags, and the bags will be loaded back into your cart. Then you can push your cart out through the magic door and leave the noisy supermarket behind you.

But you know it won't be long until you have to come back and go grocery shopping again!

Thinking and Writing About the Selection

1. Why would you want to use a coupon?

2. What will happen at the check-out counter?

3. Why should you look at the prices as you shop?

 4. Make a shopping list of five things you would need at the supermarket.

Applying the Key Skill
Interpret Graphic Aids

Read the chart. Then answer the questions on your paper. Use complete sentences.

A Shopping Trip			
	apples	cereal	milk
Julian	3	2	2
Emily	2	1	3
Ben	5	3	0
Pam	1	0	1

1. How much cereal did Julian buy?

2. Who bought more apples, Emily or Julian?

3. Who bought the most food?

4. Who bought the least amount of food?

209

SKILLS activity

CHARTS AND TABLES

Charts and tables show us facts in a different way. By looking at a chart or table we get the information we need quickly. The title of the chart or table tells us the kind of information on the chart or table.

ACTIVITY A The boys and girls made a chart to show what kinds of pets they had. Look at the chart. Use the chart to answer the questions. Write the answers on your paper. Use complete sentences.

Pets of the Boys and Girls	
Name	**Pet**
Amy	bird
Don	rabbit
Jose	dog
Mandy	cat
Peter	bird
Tami	turtle
Rosa	dog

210

1. What pet does Amy have?
2. Who has a pet turtle?
3. What pet does Don have?
4. How many children have birds as pets?
5. Who has the same pet as Rosa?

ACTIVITY B Julian and Kate decided to have a food sale to earn money for a school pet. They earned $7.50. The children bought a fish for the school aquarium.

Read the table. Use the table to answer the questions. Write the answers on your paper. Use complete sentences.

The Food Sale	
Food Sold	**Money Earned**
tacos	$3.00
apple cakes	2.50
nuts	2.00
	$7.50

1. What did Julian and Kate sell?
2. How much money did they earn selling nuts?
3. How much money did they earn selling tacos?
4. What food earned the most money?
5. What food earned the least money?

M and M

And The Big Bag

Pat Ross

After your trip to the supermarket in "Let's Go Shopping!" you may be ready to shop alone. But getting all the right things can sometimes be a little tricky. Read and see how Mimi and Mandy spend their first day shopping at The Big Bag.

M and M were ready for this day. They could read prices and signs and tricky words like *cucumber* and *pizza*.

They could count their change. They always looked each way before they crossed the street. They were ready to shop at The Big Bag alone.

They read the grocery list one more time—

"That's an easy list," said Mimi.

"Nothing to it," said Mandy.

Mandy was in charge of the list. She folded the paper and tucked it under her belt.

Mimi was in charge of the money. She pushed five dollars deep into her back pocket.

Mimi's dog Maxi ran to the door and barked. Maxi didn't want to be left behind.

Mandy and Mimi had to cross two streets to get to The Big Bag. One wide street had noisy buses and fast cars. M and M waited for the green light and the WALK sign before they crossed the street.

The Big Bag had two front doors. One
said OUT and NO BARE FEET. The other said
IN and NO DOGS ALLOWED.

"That means you," said Mimi to Maxi.
Maxi didn't like being left outside—not
one bit!

"Be a good dog!" said Mandy, and she
bent down to pat him. Just then, a piece of
paper—a piece of yellow paper—fell on
the sidewalk.

Mandy didn't see it fall.

Mimi didn't see it fall.

But Maxi did. Maxi barked at the paper.

"Come on," said Mimi.

"Maxi always makes a fuss. Just pretend you don't know him," said Mimi.

So M and M turned away, and they went into The Big Bag.

"What's first on the list?" asked Mimi.

Mandy reached under her belt. "It's gone!" she cried. "What are we going to do?"

"Who needs that list anyway? We know what to buy," said Mimi.

"Are you sure?" asked Mandy.

"Yes, I'm sure," said Mimi. "I remember *everything*."

"OK," said Mandy.

The Big Bag looked bigger than ever. There were so many rows and signs. There was so much food. They decided to start with the row that said SNACKS.

"Was popcorn on the list?" asked Mimi.

"I thought you remembered everything," said Mandy.

"Well, I *think* it was on the list," said Mimi. And she put popcorn in the cart.

"Hey! What about that new cereal that comes with the little plane inside?" asked Mimi.

"Yes," said Mandy. So Mimi put a box of the new cereal in the cart.

Soon, the cart was filled with popcorn, cereal, peanut butter plain, peanut butter crunchy, ice cream, paper cups, and toothbrushes. Mandy and Mimi got in line for the check-out counter. The cart was loaded to the very top. They looked at the five dollars. Then they looked at each other.

"We needed the list," said Mandy.

"I usually remember better," said Mimi.

"We'll never get to go shopping again if we come back with all this stuff!" cried Mandy.

"What do we do now?"

"Put it back," said Mandy.

Quickly, Mimi and Mandy put all the things from their cart back on the shelves. Then they ran for the door that said OUT. And there was Maxi with a yellow something in his mouth.

"The list!" cried Mandy.

Maxi chewed the paper. Mimi gave a dog treat to Maxi. Maxi dropped the paper. Now the yellow list was wet and sticky and dirty. It even had holes in it.

M and M went back into The Big Bag with the list. Mandy and Mimi looked at the first word and laughed. It said

b   ter

"Butter!" said Mandy, and they ran to get one butter.

The next word on the list started with a hole. Then came the letters . . . read. But that did not fool them! They knew the word was bread.

Apples was the only whole word. They picked out two good crunchy apples.

The next word on the list was trash. Then they pushed the cart quickly to trash bags.

The last word was all rubbed out. But Mandy and Mimi knew the word was milk. They picked out the coldest.

"Well, that's it," said M and M. The man at the check-out counter rang up each thing.

"That comes to four dollars and three cents," he said. Mimi gave the man behind the counter the five dollars. He gave her back ninety-seven cents.

"Come again," he said.

"Oh, we will!" they answered.

They ran outside and untied Maxi. Then M and M took turns carrying one butter, one bread, two apples, trash bags, and one milk home without stopping!

Thinking and Writing About the Selection

1. How were M and M ready for their shopping day?

2. Who was in charge of the list? Who was in charge of the money?

3. Do you think Maxi was just making a fuss when he barked at the paper? Why?

4. Why was it fun getting the things from the sticky wet list?

Applying the Key Skill
r-Controlled Vowels

Number your paper from 1 to 6. Read the first word in each row. Then find the other word in the row that has the same vowel sound. Write that word on your paper.

1. word	foot	her	farm
2. part	start	street	straw
3. horn	learn	paint	story
4. girl	noisy	work	agreed
5. hurt	gruff	bird	brag
6. stern	south	hear	worm

Supermarket, Supermarket

(A Jump Rope Rhyme)

Supermarket, supermarket,
shelves piled high
with brand-new products
for you to buy:

Vegetable soapflakes,
filtertip milk,
frozen chicken wings ready to fly,

shreddable edible paper towels,
banana detergent,
deodorant pie.

Eve Merriam

225

THE RICH MAN
and
THE SHOEMAKER

Karen Young

M and M couldn't buy everything they wanted. They had just enough money to get all the things they needed. Money does not always make people happy. Too much money can be a worry, too. Read to find out how a rich man and a poor shoemaker change places.

There was once a shoemaker who lived in a small village. The shoemaker was poor, but he was happy. Every day he worked from early morning until evening to make the money his family needed.

The shoemaker always sang as he worked. When the people of the village heard him singing, they hurried to knock on his door. Then they watched him fix old shoes and listened to his happy songs.

Next door to the shoemaker lived a rich man. He had all the things he wanted. But the rich man was still unhappy.

Night after sleepless night, he thought only about his money. He was so scared that someone would take his money that he sometimes did not fall asleep until the sun came up.

Early each morning the shoemaker got out of bed, excited about a new day. He sat at his work table and began to work and sing. The singing woke the rich man from his sleep.

The same thing happened every morning. At last the rich man began to feel sorry for himself. "With every song the shoemaker sings, my head hurts more and more!" he cried. "I cannot stand another sleepless night. My head hurts. My back hurts. This noise must stop!"

For once, the rich man thought about something other than money. "It is too bad I cannot buy sleep as I can buy food," he thought. He tried to think of a way to make the shoemaker stop singing.

Early the next morning, the shoemaker heard a knock at his door. It was the rich man. "Why would my rich neighbor come to see me?" the shoemaker asked himself. "He would not need me to fix his shoes. He could just buy new ones!"

The rich man had not come for shoes. He wanted to talk to the shoemaker about money.

"Tell me, how much money do you earn in one year?" he asked.

"One year?" the shoemaker laughed. "I'm sorry, but I don't know. It isn't worth it to keep records of my money. I don't earn enough for that."

"Well," the rich man said, "what are you paid in one day?"

"Sometimes a lot, sometimes a little," answered the shoemaker. "If I spend my money wisely, I can always get by."

The rich man tried again. "What is your fee to fix shoes?" he asked.

"A penny or two," the shoemaker said with a smile. "It isn't much, but I am always happy."

"You are the happiest man I have ever known," the rich man said. "Here! I have a surprise for you. You have earned it with all your happy songs." He gave the shoemaker a heavy bag. It was full of money. Then the rich man walked home, smiling to himself. "Now I will get some sleep!" he thought.

The excited shoemaker hurried into his house. He closed the door so that no one could see inside. Then he took the bag to his work table and began to count the money.

"One hundred pounds!" he said in surprise. "I have never seen so much money at once! If I am wise, I can make it last all my life. I will not tell anyone, not even my wife."

When the people of the village came to visit the shoemaker, they could not see in the door. "What's wrong?" they called to the shoemaker. "We are here to watch you work."

When the shoemaker heard their knock, he jumped up. He hurried to his room and pushed the money under the bed. Then he opened the door and sat down to work. But he did not sing. He thought about his money. Would it be all right under the bed? Where else could he hide it?

He picked up the money bag and hid it under the bed covers. "No one will look there," he told himself. Still he could not work. He was scared that his wife would find the money when she went to bed. At last he took the bag outside and hid it in the chicken house in the yard.

While the shoemaker looked for a place to hide his money, the rich man slept. He took a long nap. He slept all day and also a good part of the evening. It was now the shoemaker who had a sleepless night.

The shoemaker tossed and turned. "I have never known you to be so unhappy," his wife said. "What is wrong?"

"Never mind!" said the shoemaker. He thought that he would sleep, once he found a good hiding place for the money. He got out of bed and went out to the chicken house. He took the bag of money and hid it behind the door. By the time morning came, the shoemaker had not slept all night.

"It hurts me to see you this way," his wife said. "Please tell me what the matter is."

The shoemaker took the money bag from behind the door and put it on the table. "We are rich!" he told his wife. "I should be happy, but I'm not. I have never known such worry."

His wife told him, "Take the money back to the rich man. I don't mind being poor. It will be worth the money to hear you singing again."

The excited shoemaker took the bag of money and ran to his neighbor. His knock woke the rich man. "I'm sorry, but I cannot keep your one hundred pounds," the shoemaker said. "I want my happy life back. I want to sing and sleep. I have always been poor, but I have never been unhappy."

Thinking and Writing About the Selection

1. Why did the village people visit the shoemaker?

2. What did the rich man think about when he couldn't sleep?

3. What did the shoemaker think about when he couldn't sleep?

4. Why wasn't the shoemaker happy with his money?

Applying the Key Skill
Synonyms

Number your paper from 1 to 5. Read the first word in each row. Then find the word in the row that has the same or almost the same meaning. Write that word on your paper.

1. fast   slow   quick   open
2. mad   angry   bad   asleep
3. beautiful magic   pretty   better
4. loud   notice   quiet   noisy
5. letters   mail   business   clerk

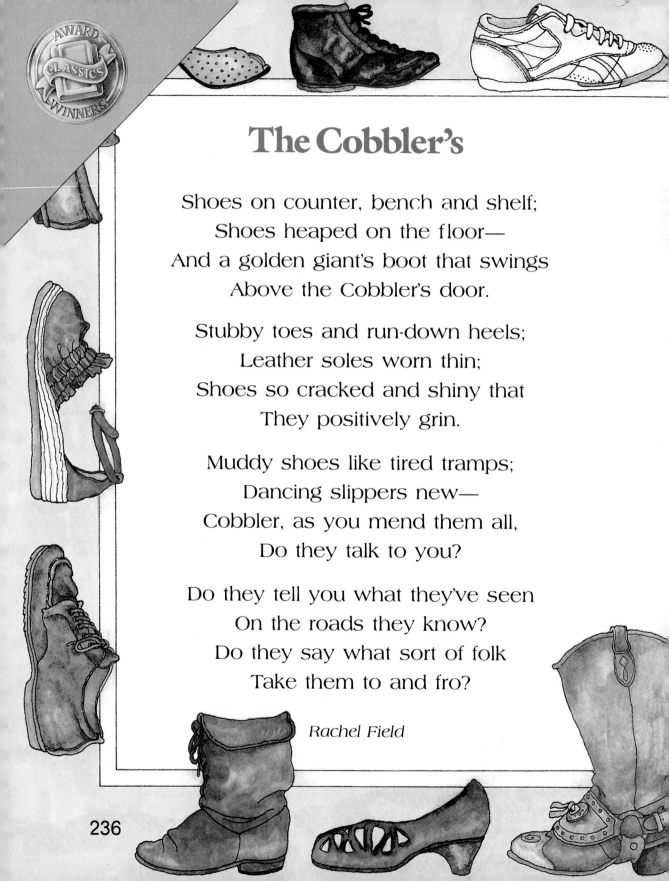

The Cobbler's

Shoes on counter, bench and shelf;
Shoes heaped on the floor—
And a golden giant's boot that swings
Above the Cobbler's door.

Stubby toes and run-down heels;
Leather soles worn thin;
Shoes so cracked and shiny that
They positively grin.

Muddy shoes like tired tramps;
Dancing slippers new—
Cobbler, as you mend them all,
Do they talk to you?

Do they tell you what they've seen
On the roads they know?
Do they say what sort of folk
Take them to and fro?

Rachel Field

237

PENNY-WISE, FUN-FOOLISH

Judy Delton

Illustrated by Giulio Maestro

Ostrich finds out that saving money may be wise, but Elephant helps Ostrich learn that spending money isn't always foolish. It can even be fun.

"Two hundred, three hundred, four hundred . . ." Ostrich counted out loud. "My bank is nearly full," she said to herself. "I can take a trip to America with Elephant." Ostrich closed her bank and locked it.

Just then she picked up the newspaper. She saw a coupon for a free photograph at Parrot's Picture Palace. She decided to cut it out. As Ostrich got her scissors, there was a knock on the door. It was Elephant.

"I have just been to the new swimming pool," he said. "It is a grand place! There are six showers, and a diving board! Wait until you see it!"

Ostrich shook her head. "I hear they charge money to get in. Why pay to swim when you can swim in the mudhole for free?"

"Some things are worth paying for," said Elephant. "Well, I must be on my way," said Elephant. "Good-by, Ostrich."

"Good-by, Elephant."

Ostrich cut out the coupon for the free photograph. Then she saw another. She cut it out, too.

The next morning Ostrich woke up early. Then she left for Parrot's Picture Palace. When she arrived, she gave Parrot her coupon.

"Be sure to smile," said Parrot. Ostrich did. Parrot snapped the picture.

"It will be ready next week."

"Thank you," said Ostrich.

Then Ostrich took another coupon from her bag. It said: BUY TEN TYPEWRITER RIBBONS AT REGULAR PRICE, GET SIX MORE FREE. BABOON'S TYPE SHOP.

Ostrich hurried to Baboon's Type Shop. "I would like to use this coupon," she said.

Ostrich bought the ribbons and started for home.

She passed by Elephant's house.

"Come in," said Elephant.

"I believe I will," said Ostrich.

She sat down on the sofa. Then she told Elephant about the photograph. She showed him the typewriter ribbons.

Elephant laughed. "But Ostrich, you don't have a typewriter."

"That's true," said Ostrich. "But I have a coupon that says: OPEN A SAVINGS ACCOUNT AND GET A TYPEWRITER FREE. I will put the money for our trip into the bank until we leave. That way I will get a free typewriter."

"I should have known," said Elephant. "By the way, the carnival is coming here on Saturday. I hope we can go together."

"I just can't," said Ostrich. "I don't want to spend the money."

"I will be glad to pay your way," said Elephant. "Please come. It will be more fun with a friend."

"No," said Ostrich. "I cannot let you spend your money on me. I am saving my money for our big trip to America."

"All you do is save," said Elephant. "Save, save, save! Can't you ever forget saving and have a good time?"

"It never hurts to have something for a rainy day," said Ostrich. "I must go home now. I have a lot to do."

When Ostrich got home, she took a nap. When she got up, she sat down to read the evening newspaper.

As Ostrich read her newspaper, a piece of paper fell to the floor. Ostrich picked it up. It said: FREE WITH THIS COUPON. ONE ADMISSION TO THE JUNGLE CARNIVAL FOR ANY OSTRICH. ALSO GOOD FOR FREE RIDES.

Ostrich ran to the telephone.
"Elephant!" she shouted. "I can go to the carnival for free! There is a coupon in my newspaper for an ostrich. Now we can go together!"

"I'm glad," said Elephant. "I will meet you at nine o'clock tomorrow morning."

Elephant waved when he saw Ostrich the next morning. "You are right on time!" he said.

"Yes," said Ostrich. "I am so excited. I have never been to a carnival. They always charge admission, you know."

When they reached the carnival gate, Elephant paid Zebra the admission fee. He also bought a book of tickets.

Then Ostrich gave Zebra her coupon. Zebra gave her a book of tickets.

Elephant and Ostrich walked toward the rides.

"What should we try first?" asked Elephant.

"The Ferris wheel," said Ostrich.

245

Ostrich and Elephant rode the Ferris wheel.

"That was scary!" said Ostrich. "But I liked it!"

Then they rode on the merry-go-round. After that they went for a ride in the rocket.

"That was fun," she said.

Elephant and Ostrich played all day. Later that night they started for home.

"My, oh, my!" chattered Ostrich. "I have never had such a good time."

"I'm glad," said Elephant.

"I'm sorry you had to pay," said Ostrich. "Too bad there wasn't a coupon for elephants. That would have been good for you."

Elephant looked silly. "Er—Ostrich— there is something I—er—should tell you. Ah—I put that coupon in your newspaper. I paid Zebra for your tickets ahead of time."

Ostrich stopped walking. "You paid!" she said.

"Yes," said Elephant. "But didn't you have a good time?"

"Why, yes. I can't remember when I had more fun! But you paid for both of us!"

"Sometimes spending money is worthwhile," said Elephant.

Ostrich thought for a time. Then she said, "What are you doing next Saturday? Well—ah—I would like to try that new swimming pool. I could swim better in a swimming pool than I can in the mudhole."

"Fine!" said Elephant. "We will go together!"

"I will pay," said Ostrich.

Elephant laughed. "I will let you."

Thinking and Writing About the Selection

1. What did Ostrich see in the newspaper?
2. Was it silly for Ostrich to buy typewriter ribbons if she didn't have a typewriter? Why?
3. How can you tell that Elephant and Ostrich were good friends?
4. What do you think penny-wise, fun-foolish means?

Applying the Key Skill
Initial Consonant Digraphs

Use the letters below to complete the sentences. Write the sentences on your paper.

ch   th   sh   wh

1. Ostrich ___ought that she could go to the carnival for free.
2. They always ___arge admission for ___e carnival.
3. Elephant put on silly ___oes for the ___ow.
4. "___ere is your coupon?" asked Zebra.

Jasper
Makes
Music

Betty Horvath

Have you ever wanted something so much that you could not think of anything else? Read and find out if Jasper can make his wish come true.

Jasper wanted a guitar—a real guitar of his own that he could carry around and strum and make music with. He had wanted it for a long time. Then he saw the guitar in the window of Anderson's Music Store and he knew suddenly and certainly that this was the very guitar he wanted. He had to have it.

But tied to the neck of the guitar was a price tag. It said $29.95. In all Jasper's eight years he had never had that much money. Right now he didn't have *any*.

He turned his pockets inside out hopefully. One pocket held a gum wrapper and a piece of string, and the other had nothing in it but a sticky cough drop. No money at all. Not a single penny. Jasper pressed his face against the window until his nose was squashed flat, and he looked and looked.

251

All the way home he thought about the guitar. He hummed a little, and his fingers made strumming movements.

"If I had that old guitar," he told himself, "I could sit out on the front-porch steps and watch the moon come up, and sing."

He ran to find his mother.

"There's something I need," Jasper told her.

His mother looked at Jasper's feet. "I'll bet I can guess," she said. "You need a new pair of shoes."

"No," said Jasper, "that's not it. I need a guitar."

His mother laughed. "No, Jasper. You just *want* a guitar. What you *need* is shoes."

Jasper turned away sadly. He didn't need shoes. He didn't even want shoes. What he needed and wanted was a guitar, a real guitar of his own that he could carry around and make music with.

Jasper went looking for his father. He found him up on a ladder putting on storm windows.

"Dad," Jasper called up to him, "there's something I need."

"There's something I need, too, son," his father said. "Run and get me the hammer."

Jasper brought him the hammer, and began again. "There's something I need. I need a guitar."

"A guitar?" His father grunted. "What do you need a guitar for?"

"To make music," Jasper said.

"We've got a radio for that," his father said, and he began hammering so loudly that Jasper couldn't tell him about the guitar in the window of Anderson's Music Store that looked as if it belonged to him.

"Maybe I can make a guitar," Jasper thought.

He found an empty cigar box, and his big brother Paul helped him nail a thin board to it for a neck. Then they strung it with rubber bands. Jasper took it out on the front-porch steps and started to sing and play. But no matter how hard he tried, he and his guitar just didn't seem to be singing the same song. It didn't sound like a guitar at all. It sounded like an old cigar box strung with rubber bands, and Jasper put it down.

A week went by. Jasper got a new pair of shoes.

A month went by. He got a winter jacket because it was getting colder now. Winter was coming. Most evenings it was too cold, anyway, for him to sit out on the front-porch steps and sing and watch the moon come up. Every day after school, no matter how cold it was, Jasper walked down to Anderson's Music Store to see if the guitar was still in the window. It always was.

One Saturday morning when Jasper woke up, he heard Grandpa's voice downstairs. "Get up, Jasper! We've got work to do today."

Jasper dressed hurriedly. Working with Grandpa was a treat. He put on his oldest shirt and the blue jeans with patches, and clattered downstairs.

"What are we going to do today, Grandpa?" he asked.

Grandpa pointed out the window. "See those squirrels? They know winter is coming. They're busy storing up food for the winter, and that's what we're going to do, too. We're going to be squirrels."

Jasper thought about being a squirrel. He thought about Grandpa being a squirrel. He almost laughed out loud.

Then he saw that one whole corner of the kitchen floor was covered with jar after jar of tomatoes, corn, peas, beans, and peaches that his mother had been canning all summer long.

"I know!" he said, pointing. "These are our 'acorns' and we're going to store them in the cellar."

"Right!" said Grandpa. "But before we store our food away we've got a job to do. We have to clean the cellar out first."

He handed Jasper a broom, and he and Jasper went down the back steps into the cool, dim, cob-webby little room under the house.

They began to work. It was hard work sweeping the floor and dusting off all the shelves, but it was kind of like a treasure hunt, too. Jasper kept finding things he hadn't seen for a long time. He found his baseball that had been missing most of the summer. He found an old roller skate—some pieces of chalk—a few marbles. Then, over in the corner, Jasper saw the handle of something half hidden behind some boxes. When he pulled it out, he was holding a small shovel.

"Look what I found, Grandpa!" he shouted.

Grandpa picked it up. "Why, I believe you've found the magic shovel I gave your daddy when he was about your size."

"A magic shovel! What's magic about it?" Jasper asked, and his eyes were big with excitement.

"It's magic because you can get things you wish for with it. If I remember rightly, it got your daddy a bicycle."

"Oh, boy!" said Jasper, thinking about the guitar. "How does it work?"

"Well, that's the funny thing," Grandpa said. "Part of the magic depends on the person who owns it. Part of the magic depends on the weather, too, because it's a snow shovel. You'd be surprised how much money a boy can earn shoveling snow— especially if he has a magic shovel." Grandpa smiled, and he winked at Jasper.

Jasper winked back.

When they had finished storing all the jars in the cellar, Jasper polished his magic shovel until it shone. Then he stood it on the back porch to wait for the first snowy day.

While he was waiting, he made a few
business calls.

Up and down the street he went,
knocking on doors and asking his neighbors
very politely if he could be their winter
snow-shoveler.

"I've got a magic shovel," he told them,
"and if I wish hard enough and work hard
enough I'll earn enough money to buy a guitar."

Mrs. Adams said No, she didn't need a
snow-shoveler.

Mrs. Hill said Maybe, sometimes.

Mr. Bixler said he did his own shoveling.

261

But Mrs. James and Miss Daniels and Mr. Arthur said Yes, Jasper could shovel their snow all winter long for fifty cents every single time it snowed. And of course Jasper told his mother that he would shovel free for his own family.

Then Jasper did one more thing. He needed a bank to keep his money in. He took an empty baking powder can, covered it with white paper, and printed on it with a red crayon, GUITAR MONEY.

He was all ready for the first snowfall.

Then one day the snow began to fall.

It fell and fell and fell.

And Jasper shoveled and shoveled and shoveled.

And he whistled while he worked, because he knew that by the time it was warm enough again to sit out on the front-porch steps and sing, he'd have a real guitar of his own to carry around and strum and make music with.

Pennies and Presents

Through reading the stories in this unit you have learned about how to earn, save, and borrow money. You might say that you have learned something about business. Perhaps you are ready to begin saving for something. It may be for you or for someone else.

Thinking and Writing About *Pennies and Presents*

1. In the stories "Bit By Bit" and in "The Best Train Set Ever," both Rosa and Peter wanted something. How did each one get what he or she wanted?

2. What did the shoemaker learn from the rich man in the story "The Rich Man and the Shoemaker"?

3. In "Penny-Wise, Fun-Foolish" how did Elephant show Ostrich that spending can be fun?

4. In "M and M and the Big Bag" what did Mimi and Mandy learn about shopping?

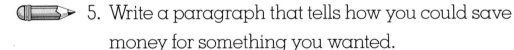 5. Write a paragraph that tells how you could save money for something you wanted.

This glossary can help you find out the meaning of words in this book that you may not know.

The words are listed in alphabetical order. Guide words at the top of each page tell you the first and last word on the page. Each word is divided into syllables.

The definitions are adapted from the Macmillan *Beginning Dictionary*.

A

a·bout In regard to; of; concerning. That book is about Ben Franklin.

ac·count A spoken or written statement; a report; a record of money spent or received; a sum of money deposited with a bank. Mr. Long put one hundred dollars in his bank account.

a·cross From one side to the other; on or to the other side. A bridge across the water led from one city to the other.

act One of the parts of a play; something that is done; to do something or move; to perform in a play. The first act of the play takes place in a castle.

ad·mire To feel a great respect for; to look at or speak of with pleasure and approval. I admire the art of Alexander Calder.

ad·mis·sion The act of allowing to come in or enter; the price that one has to pay to come in. The price of the admission to the show was three dollars.

ad·ver·tise·ment A public announcement describing what is special or good about something. We saw the advertisement for a book sale.

af·ter Following the time that; later; in the rear; behind. After I go to bed, I go to sleep.

af·ter·noon The part of the day between noon and evening. The children will come home from school in the afternoon.

age The amount of time that a person, animal, or thing has lived or existed. Ann will soon be nine years of <u>age</u>.

a·greed Had the same idea; said "yes" to something. The children <u>agreed</u> on what job each would have.

al·lowed Gave permission to do or have something; added or took an amount for a special reason. Oliver's parents <u>allowed</u> him to stay up late.

al·most Very close to; nearly. Freddy <u>almost</u> always plays ball after school.

a·lone Not near or with another or others. When the children went to school, their mother was <u>alone</u> in the house.

al·ways All the time; every time. Do you <u>always</u> look before you cross the street?

A·mer·i·ca Another name for the United States. We live in <u>America</u>.

a·mount What something adds up to; total quantity. The <u>amount</u> of water needed to make the cereal was one cup.

an·gry Feeling or showing anger. We were scared when the man spoke in an <u>angry</u> voice.

an·swers Writes or speaks in reply to something. Ted always gives <u>answers</u> when people ask him things.

an·y·more At the present; from now on. When I get tired, I can't work <u>anymore</u>.

an·y·one Any person whatever; anybody. "Does <u>anyone</u> want to come with me to the park?" Mother asked the children.

ap·ples Roundish fruit with red, yellow, or green skin. The children usually have <u>apples</u> to eat after school.

a·round In a circle and back; along the outer edge of; on all sides of; so as to surround. The children ran from the front door <u>around</u> the house and back again.

ar·rived Came to a place. We arrived at school at nine o'clock.

art Painting, drawing, and sculpture, or anything that has beauty or meaning. Painting and music are two kinds of art.

a·sleep Sleeping. Mother said, "Don't wake the baby when she is asleep."

B

ba·boon A large monkey that has a face like that of a dog. You might see a baboon if you go to the zoo.

bare Without covering or clothing; naked; empty. When fall comes, the trees are bare.

barked The short, sharp sound that a dog makes. The dog barked when the man walked up to the porch.

beau·ti·ful Pleasing to look at or hear. Maria liked to look at the beautiful painting.

been Had reality; existed or lived; took place; happened; remained or continued as before. Ben has been thinking about finding a job for some time.

be·fore Previous to the time when; in front of; ahead of. You should look up and down the street before you cross it.

be·gins Starts; does the first part of something. When it begins to grow dark, the children go home.

be·hind At the back of; later than; after; not on time; late; slow; in a place just left. Amanda was behind in her school work.

be·lieve To have trust or faith in the truth of; to think, suppose. I believe that I can save two dollars in a week.

belt A strip or band of cloth, leather, or other material. Nan made a <u>belt</u> of shells.

best Of the highest quality; superior to all others; in the most successful way; something of the highest quality or excellence. Pam has many friends, but Jill is her <u>best</u> friend.

birth·day The day on which a person is born. Tami will be eight on her next <u>birthday</u>.

black·bird Any of various birds that are mostly black. A <u>blackbird</u> has dark feathers.

blue The color of the clear sky in the daytime; having the color blue. Joanne likes <u>blue</u> better than any other color.

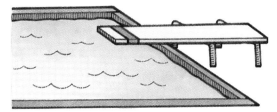

board A long, flat piece of wood; a flat piece of wood or other material used for some special purpose. Many games are played on a <u>board</u>.

bor·row To take something from another person with the understanding that it must be given back. Linda asked Leo if she could <u>borrow</u> his skates.

both The two; the one and the other. <u>Both</u> Billy and Jenny can swim.

bot·tles Containers to hold liquids. Mrs. Long filled the <u>bottles</u> with milk for the baby.

box·es Containers used to hold things. We carried home two <u>boxes</u>. One box had dog food, the other had cat food.

braids Strips made by weaving together three or more long pieces of hair, straw, or cloth. Beth didn't want a haircut. She wanted to keep her long <u>braids</u>.

269

break To make come apart by force; to harm or damage. The radio may break if you drop it.

break·fast The first meal of the day. Many people have toast, eggs, and something to drink for breakfast.

bring To cause something or someone to come with you; to cause something to come or happen. Ted asked Jane to bring her sister with her when she came to his house.

broth·er A boy or man having the same parents as another person. Amanda's brother, Jack, is the only boy in the family.

busi·ness The work one does to earn a living; matter or affair. My mother's business is thinking up advertisements.

buy To get something by paying money for it; to purchase. Jane saved her money to buy a birthday present for her brother.

C

ca·boose A railroad car that is at the end of a freight train. Men who work on the train sometimes ride in the caboose.

Ca·lam·i·ty bank A bank that was sold in the early 1900s. A calamity is an accident.

Cal·der, Al·ex·an·der An American artist. The art of Alexander Calder has a message for many people.

card A flat piece of stiff paper that may have words, numbers, or some kind of design on it. If you have a library card you can take books out of the library.

car·ni·val A fair or festival that has games, rides, and other amusements. There will be animals, rides, and things to eat at the carnival.

car·ried Held something while moving it. Jerry <u>carried</u> his books to school.

cart A strong wagon with two wheels that is used to carry a load; a light vehicle with four wheels that is pushed by a person. We filled the shopping <u>cart</u> with food at the supermarket.

cart·wheel A kind of jump from one's feet to one's hands and back again. You use your hands and feet to turn a <u>cartwheel</u>.

cas·tle A large building or group of buildings having high thick walls with towers. The king and queen lived in the <u>castle</u>.

cat·tail A tall plant that grows in marshes. Do you know how the top of a <u>cattail</u> feels?

cel·lo A musical instrument that is like a violin but larger and lower in tone. A <u>cello</u> is a kind of box with strings that is played to make music.

ce·re·al A food that is made from grains such as wheats, oats, rye, barley, and rice. We eat <u>cereal</u> with milk for breakfast.

cer·tain·ly Without a doubt; surely. The teacher told Ramón, "You <u>certainly</u> do read well!"

charge To have or ask as a price; the price asked for something. The man said he would <u>charge</u> ten dollars to fix the clock.

check-out A checking out, as in a supermarket; a place for checking out. We took our cart to the <u>check-out</u> counter.

271

chewed Crushed and ground something with the teeth. Mother was angry when the dog <u>chewed</u> the rug.

child A son or daughter; a young boy or girl. The little <u>child</u> cried and asked for its mother and father.

chil·dren More than one child. The <u>children</u> went to school on a bus.

Chi·na Pig bank A colorful, decorated pig made of china or fine pottery and used as a bank. Saving is fun if you have a <u>China Pig bank</u> to keep your money in.

cir·cus A show with trained animals and acrobats, clowns, and other people who do special things. A <u>circus</u> is a show put on by people and animals in a big tent.

clerk A person who sells goods to a customer in a store. The <u>clerk</u> asked us if she could help us find what we were looking for.

coach A railroad car for passengers. It was fun to ride in the <u>coach</u> and look out at the land as the train passed through.

code Any set of signals, words, or symbols used to send messages. You can use a <u>code</u> to write a secret message.

cold·est Having the lowest temperature; chilliest. Last Saturday was the <u>coldest</u> day of the winter so far.

col·lec·tion A gathering together. Miles has a huge <u>collection</u> of games that he likes to play.

col·or Red, blue, or yellow. All the other colors are a combination or shade of red, blue, or yellow; to give color to. The color red is sometimes a sign for "stop," "hot," or "on."

com·put·ers Electronic machines that can solve difficult mathematical and logical problems at very high speeds. People use computers to help them with work at school and on the job.

coun·ter A long table. The clerk put the necklace on the counter so we could see it.

cou·pon A ticket or part of a ticket. The coupon was good for twenty cents toward the price of the cereal.

cov·ered Put something over or on; hidden or protected. Snow covered the houses, the trees, and the ground.

crunch·y Making a crackling sound. The apples are good and crunchy.

cu·cum·ber A long, green vegetable with white flesh and many seeds inside. Mother bought a cucumber at the grocery.

D

dark Having little or no light. It is dark at night, even when the moon is out.

daugh·ter A female child. Father and Mother's first child was a daughter. They named her Mary.

dear Much or greatly loved. Ben wrote, "Dear Andy," as he began his letter.

de·cid·ed Made up one's mind. Ed decided to go shopping.

die·sel A vehicle powered by a diesel engine. The truck was a diesel, and the car was, too.

dif·fer·ent Not alike or similar; not the same; separate. Night is <u>different</u> from day.

di·rec·tions Orders or instructions on how to do something or how to act; the lines or courses along which something moves, faces, or lies. If you want something you make to turn out well, you should follow the <u>directions</u>.

dirt·y Soiled; not clean. Meg has to clean her room when it gets <u>dirty</u>.

dol·lars Units of money in the United States, worth one hundred cents. Mrs. Yee paid ten <u>dollars</u> for the necklace.

drag·on An imaginary beast that is supposed to look something like a giant lizard with claws and wings. A <u>dragon</u> is a huge animal that people have made up.

drug·store A store where medicines and drugs are sold. Beth found a birthday card for Harry at the <u>drugstore</u>.

E

ea·gle A large, powerful bird that hunts and feeds on small animals. There is a picture of an <u>eagle</u> on the back of a quarter.

ear·ly In or near the beginning. Our family goes to bed <u>early</u> at night and gets up <u>early</u> in the morning.

earned To get as pay for work done. Robin <u>earned</u> money by having a newspaper route.

eas·y Needing only a little work; not hard to do. It is <u>easy</u> to turn a cartwheel once you learn how.

else Other; different; if not; otherwise. Mike told Kate, "Someone else I know looks just like you."

emp·ty Having nothing in it; without what is usually inside. When I opened the box, I found that it was empty.

end To bring or come to an end; the last part. Jerry watched the show to the end and went to bed when it was over.

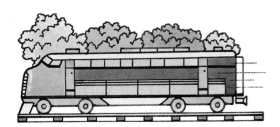

en·gine A machine that uses energy to run other machines; a machine that pulls a railroad train. The train had nine cars behind the engine.

e·nough As much or as many as needed. Will there be enough chairs for everyone?

er·rands Short trips to do something. Mark runs many errands for his mother and father.

es·pe·cial·ly More than usually; particularly. Jerry likes peanut butter especially well.

e·ven Still; yet; even though it may seem unlikely. Meg is still my friend, even though I am angry with her.

ev·er At any time. Do you ever listen to music?

ex·cit·ed Stirred up; aroused. Everyone in the city was excited about the carnival.

ex·pect To think; to suppose; to look forward to; to want something because it is right or necessary. Mother and Father expect Ted to keep his room neat and clean.

F

feath·ers The light growths that cover a bird's skin. A bird's feathers are like a coat for the bird.

felt Touched; found out about by touching or handling; thought or believed. Mona felt the water to see if it was hot.

Fer·ris wheel A large revolving wheel with seats hung from its rim. The boys were excited by their ride on the Ferris wheel.

few Not many; not many persons or things. A few of my friends have been to Mexico.

fif·ty Five times ten; 50. The bus Jack rides to school holds fifty children.

fin·gers The five separate parts at the end of the hand. People use their fingers to do many things.

fin·ished Brought to an end; came to an end; completed; used up completely. Jane finished the letter and put it in the mail.

flew Moved through the air. The bird flew from the tree to its nest on the porch.

folded Bent or doubled over on itself; brought together close to the body. Father folded the newspaper and put it down.

fol·low To go or come after; to act according to; to go along. Leo will follow the rabbit's tracks to find out where it went.

fool A person who does not have good sense; to trick; to be silly; to joke or tease. I will use a deep voice to fool you.

fool·ish Without good sense; unwise; silly. It is foolish to buy something that will soon break.

four One more than three. Two and two make four.

Frank·lin, Ben 1706–1790. American statesman, scientist, author, and inventor. Ben Franklin wrote a book about his life.

G

giv·en Handed over or granted to another or others. After Mike had <u>given</u> the present to Pam, she said, "Thanks!"

gold A heavy yellow metal used to make jewelry and coins. The pretty necklace was made of <u>gold</u>.

gone Moved from one place to another. The bus had <u>gone</u> by the time Nan got to the bus stop, so she had to wait for the next one.

grand Large and splendid; very good or excellent. The children thought a trip to the zoo was a <u>grand</u> idea.

gro·cer·y A store that sells food and household supplies. **gro·cer·ies.** Food and other things sold by a grocer. Eddie stopped at the <u>grocery</u> to buy cereal.

guess To form an opinion without having enough knowledge or facts to be sure; to get the correct answer by guessing; to think, believe, or suppose. Can you <u>guess</u> how many books are in the library?

H

hair·cut The act or style of cutting the hair. Mother gave Emily a <u>haircut</u> and cut off her braids.

hap·pen To take place; occur; occur by chance. What do you think will <u>happen</u> if you water the seeds in the ground?

hard Needing or using much effort; solid and firm to the touch, not soft. Sam finds it <u>hard</u> to do all the things he wants to in one day.

has To have. Peter <u>has</u> a new baby brother.

hat·ed Disliked very much. The little boy <u>hated</u> having a haircut.

heav·y Having great weight. It was hard to move the <u>heavy</u> boxes.

hers The one or ones that belong or relate to her. Scott reads his book, and Gloria reads <u>hers</u>.

hey A word used to attract attention or to show surprise or pleasure. "<u>Hey</u>!" shouted the man. "<u>Watch</u> where you are going!"

honk·ers A word that is sometimes used for geese. <u>Honkers</u> are birds with a cry that sounds like a horn.

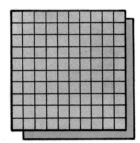

hun·dred Ten times ten; 100. Cindy says she had read a <u>hundred</u> books.

hur·ried Done or made quickly or too quickly. Julian <u>hurried</u> through breakfast to get to school on time.

hurts Causes pain or injury; feels pain. The loud noise <u>hurts</u> my ears.

I

ice·berg A very large piece of floating ice. Penguins were living on the <u>iceberg</u>.

i·dea A thought, belief, or opinion formed in the mind; the purpose of something. The boys had a good <u>idea</u> for making money.

I'll Contraction for "I will" and "I shall." "<u>I'll</u> help you with those books," said the librarian.

I'm Contraction for I am. I have saved five dollars so far, and <u>I'm</u> going to save even more.

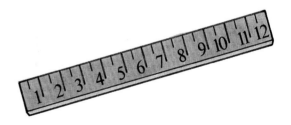

inch·es Measures of length that equals 1/12 of a foot. Do you know how many <u>inches</u> there are in a foot?

in·for·ma·tion Knowledge or facts about something. Ted wants to find <u>information</u> about where bears live.

278

in·side On, in, or towards the inside; within. Jeff found out what was <u>inside</u> the box when he opened it.

in·ter·est A desire or eagerness to know about or take part in something; money that is paid for the use of a larger sum of money. Gloria was happy to earn <u>interest</u> on the money she put in the bank.

is·land A body of land that is completely surrounded by water. An <u>island</u> has water all around it.

I've Contraction for I have. <u>I've</u> decided to go to the playground with Mona.

J

job A position of work; employment; something that has to be done. Father works in Newport, where he has a <u>job</u> painting signs.

jun·gle Land in tropical areas that is covered with a thick mass of trees, vines, and bushes. Elephants, birds, and many other animals are found in the <u>jungle</u>.

K

king A man who rules a country. The <u>king</u> had a huge kingdom to look after.

king·dom A country that is ruled by a king or queen. A trip through the <u>kingdom</u> took a very long time.

knew Understood clearly; was familiar with. Meg <u>knew</u> the answers to everything the teacher asked.

known Understood clearly; was certain of the facts or truth of; was familiar with. If Andy had <u>known</u> it was going to rain, he would have stayed home.

L

least Smallest; at the very minimum. At <u>least</u> twenty children answered the advertisement for a summer job.

lend To let someone have or use something for a while. Jason's parents said they would <u>lend</u> him the money for a pet.

let·ter A written message; a mark that stands for a speech sound. Ed wrote Kate a <u>letter</u> to tell her about his trip.

li·brar·i·an A person who is in charge of a library. A <u>librarian</u> can help you find books in a library.

li·brar·y A collection of books and magazines. Jeff found a good book to read in the <u>library</u>.

lis·tened Tried to hear; paid attention in order to hear. Sue <u>listened</u> as her father spoke.

M

mag·a·zines A printed collection of stories, articles, and pictures, usually bound in a paper cover. Most libraries have <u>magazines</u>, as well as books, to read.

mag·ic The art of pretending to be able to do something that is not usually possible, by using special charms or spells; the art or skill of doing tricks to entertain people. Mimi knows how to do quite a few <u>magic</u> tricks.

man·y Made up of a large number; a large number. <u>Many</u> people live in a big city.

mar·ket A place or store where food or goods are sold. We went to the <u>market</u> to buy food for dinner.

me·chan·i·cal Using or having to do with machines. The baby has a <u>mechanical</u> chair that goes when you wind it up.

me·dia cen·ter A <u>media center</u> is a room that may have books, records, games, and computers.

mer·ry-go-round A round platform that has wooden animals and seats on which people ride while the platform turns. Ted liked the <u>merry-go-round</u> best of all the rides at <u>the carnival.</u>

mes·sage Words sent from one person to another. "If you will write your <u>message</u> on this paper, I will give it to my mother," said Sue.

mes·sen·ger A person who delivers messages or runs errands. The <u>messenger</u> arrived with a package for Tim.

milk A white liquid food produced by glands in female mammals. Jerry and Mandy drink a lot of <u>milk</u> every day.

mill·er A person who owns or operates a mill for grinding grain. We make bread with what the <u>miller</u> ground.

mon·ey The coins and paper currency of a country. Gloria saved her <u>money</u> to pay for the new skates.

morn·ing The first part of the day, which ends at noon. We get up in the <u>morning</u> and eat breakfast.

most Greatest in number, amount, or degree; nearly all. Some of the girls are reading, but <u>most</u> of them are playing a game.

move To change the place or direction of something; to put into motion. Dan helped his mother <u>move</u> the chair from the room to the porch.

mu·sic A pleasing or beautiful combination of sounds. Music is made up of many sounds that please the ear.

must Should; have to; need to. We must return the books that we borrow from the library.

my·self The form used to refer to **I** or **me** in a sentence. I can read the book by myself.

N

near·ly Almost; all but. Tim will be five next week. His birthday is nearly here.

neck·lace A string of beads or other piece of jewelry worn around the neck for decoration. Mother took the necklace and put it on over her head.

neigh·bor·hood A small area or district in a town or city where people live. Most of my friends live in my neighborhood.

nei·ther Not either; nor; not either one. I don't like carrots, and neither does Jane.

New York Ci·ty The largest city in the United States. Many people visit New York City.

New·port A city in Rhode Island. Carlos lived in Newport.

news·pa·pers Printed sheets of paper that contain news, interest stories, opinions on local and national happenings, and advertising. My mother reads two newspapers every day.

nick·el A coin that is worth five cents. Mrs. Long paid for the carrots and got a nickel in change.

nine·ty-nine The number that is nine times ten plus nine. Tom has ninety-nine dollars. He needs one more to make one hundred.

nine·ty-sev·en The number that is nine times ten plus seven. My mother's grandmother is ninety-seven.

noise A sound that is loud and harsh. The people at the game yelled and shouted and made a lot of noise.

nois·y Making much noise. A playground is usually a noisy place.

none Not one; not any. None of the children could find Newport on the map.

no·tice To become aware of; observe. Did you notice the new stop sign?

num·ber The total amount of things in a group; how many there are of something. Tell me the number of children in this room.

O

old Having lived or existed for a long period of time. Mr. Bloom has many old coins in his collection that date back to the early 1800s.

once One time; in the time past; before; one single time. We once lived in the city, but we don't live there anymore.

or·der A command to do something; the way in which things are arranged; to tell to do something. **in order to** So as to be able to. In order to make a kite, you need paper, string, sticks, and glue.

os·trich A large two-toed bird that has a long neck, long strong legs, and a small flat head. An ostrich can run very fast, but it cannot fly.

oth·er Different from the one or ones already mentioned; not the same. Jason and the <u>other</u> boys were playing soccer.

our Of or belonging to us. Emily and I feed <u>our</u> pets.

o·ver·bought Bought too much or too many. When Freddy bought fifty pencils for school, he <u>overbought</u>.

P

pack·age A thing or group of things packed, wrapped up, or tied together; a box, case, or other thing in which something is packed. A very big <u>package</u> arrived in the mail.

paint A mixture of coloring matter and water, oil, or some other liquid; to cover with paint. We will use green <u>paint</u> to <u>paint</u> the roof.

pal·ace A very large, grand building where a king, queen, or other ruler lives. The poor man went to the <u>palace</u> to visit the king.

pa·per A material that is used for writing, printing, wrapping things, covering walls, and many other purposes; a piece of paper. The girls made a kite out of <u>paper</u>, string, sticks, and glue.

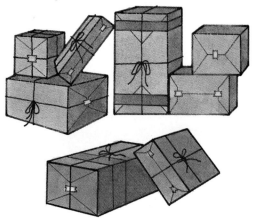

par·cels Things wrapped up; bundles or packages. We didn't know what was in the <u>parcels</u> that came in the mail.

par·ents People who are fathers or mothers. Mary, John, and their <u>parents</u> moved to a new house.

par·rot A bird with a wide curved bill, a long pointed tail, and glossy, brightly colored feathers. Have you ever heard a parrot say something?

patch A small area that is different from what is around it. The pony had a patch of white on its back.

Patz·cua·ro, Mex·i·co A city in Mexico which is on a lake. My friend lives in Patzcuaro, Mexico.

pea·nut but·ter A soft, creamy food made from ground, roasted peanuts. Most children like peanut butter and bread.

pen·cils Long, thin tools for writing or drawing, usually made of sticks of graphite enclosed in a covering of wood. The children wrote on their paper with pencils.

pen·guins Sea birds whose feathers are black or gray on the back and white on the chest. Penguins are large birds that can't fly. They live in places where there is ice and snow.

pen·ny A coin that is worth one cent. Can you think of anything you can buy with a penny?

pho·to·graph A picture that is made by using a camera. Jan took a photograph of the animals at the zoo.

pic·ture A painting, drawing, or photograph that represents a person or thing. Kate will draw a picture of what she thinks a dragon looks like.

piece A part that has been broken, cut, or torn from something; a single thing that is part of a whole; to join the parts or pieces of. John said he would break the rock in two and give a piece to Kate.

piz·za An Italian dish that is made of a flat baked crust topped with tomato sauce and cheese and sometimes also with mushrooms. It is fun to go out to eat pizza.

pock·et A small bag or pouch sewn into or on clothes. Scott took the money and put it in his pocket.

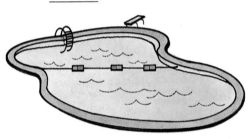

pool A tank of water to swim in; a small amount of any liquid. We have a new swimming pool in our village.

poor Having little money; bad. Freddy was poor because he had no money.

pop·corn A kind of corn having kernels that burst open with a pop when heated. John and Sally like to eat popcorn when they go to the show.

porch A roofed area built onto a house. Jeff sat on the porch at the front of his house and looked up and down the street.

pounds Units of weight, each equal to sixteen ounces; units of money in certain countries. The man paid ten pounds for new shoes.

pres·ent Something given. Oliver's parents gave him ten dollars as a present.

pre·tend To claim; to give a false show; to make believe. When we play, we sometimes pretend to be people in books.

prof·it The amount of money left after all the costs of running a business or making or selling something have been paid. Mrs. Yee made a profit of ten dollars on each telephone she sold.

pub·lic Having to do with or for all the people. Our city has a public library and a public school.

Q

quar·ter A coin equal to twenty-five cents. Mr. Raymond needed a quarter to make a telephone call.

queen A woman who rules a kingdom. The queen gave the poor man some gold.

R

ra·di·o A way of sending messages, music, or other sounds by electric waves; a device for receiving or sending such sounds. We turned on the radio to find out if it would snow.

read·y Prepared for use or action; willing; likely. We will leave for our trip as soon as we are ready.

re·al·ly In fact; actually; truly; very. The boys pretend that the old house is a castle, but it really isn't.

rec·ords A written account of something; a disk on which music or other sounds have been recorded to be played back on a phonograph. Sally likes to listen to records with singing.

red-winged Having red wings. A red-winged blackbird has a patch of red feathers in two places.

reg·u·lar Normal; usual; happening again and again at the same time. With a coupon, things do not cost as much as the <u>regular</u> price.

re·mem·bers Brings back or recalls to the mind. At first Jim doesn't know where his coat is, then he <u>remembers</u> he left it at school.

re·port An account or statement about something; to make or give a report; to present oneself. Mr. Raymond and Mr. Pompey <u>report</u> for work at eight o'clock.

rest Something that is left; remainder; others; to stop work or activity. We go to school from eight until three o'clock, then for the <u>rest</u> of the day we play.

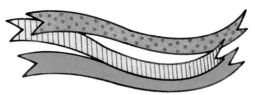

rib·bons Bands of cloth, paper, or other material, used for decoration. Mother tied <u>ribbons</u> on Amanda's braids.

Ring·ling Broth·ers Bar·num and Bail·ey Cir·cus A circus started in the early 1900s which became the most famous circus in America. We went to see the <u>Ringling Brothers Barnum and Bailey Circus</u>.

rock·et A device that is driven forward by a stream of hot gases that are released from the rear. We watched the <u>rocket</u> go up into the air.

row A series of people or things arranged in a line; a line of chairs or seats. We sat in the first <u>row</u> to watch the play.

S

Sat·ur·day The seventh day of the week. We don't go to school on <u>Saturday</u>.

scis·sors A tool used for cutting. We will use <u>scissors</u> to cut the paper, string, and ribbons.

screamed Made a loud, shrill, piercing cry or sound. The children <u>screamed</u> when a dragon came out in the second act of the play.

sec·ond Next after the first; below the first or best; another. "My <u>second</u> name is Anne," said Betty Anne, "but most people just call me Betty."

sharp Having an edge or point that cuts easily; not rounded. A cat has <u>sharp</u> claws and can scratch.

shelves Pieces of wood or metal fastened to a wall or frame, used to hold books, dishes, and other things. When Greg and Ann finish reading the books, they will put them back on the <u>shelves</u>.

shoe·mak·er A person who makes or repairs shoes and other footwear. Kate asked the <u>shoemaker</u> to fix her shoes.

shook Moved up and down or from side to side; trembled or caused to tremble. The wind <u>shook</u> the house and the trees.

shop·ping Visiting stores in order to look at and buy goods. Father and Mary went <u>shopping</u> for a new radio.

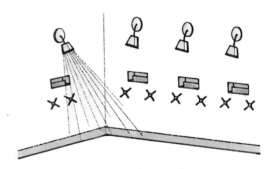

show·ers Short falls of rain; baths in which water is sprayed on a person from an overhead fixture. There are six <u>showers</u> in our gym at school.

side·ways Toward or from one side. Meg asked Tom to face front and step right to move <u>sideways</u>.

289

sing·ing Making words or sound with musical tones. The children are singing a song that they wrote.

slow·ly In a manner that is not fast or quick. Gloria woke slowly. It always took her a long time to wake up.

smil·ing Having or giving an expression of the face made by turning up the corners of the mouth. Jenny was smiling and laughing because she was happy.

sold Gave something in return for money. The man sold Fred the pencils for a quarter.

song A piece of music that is sung. A song is made up of words and music.

sor·ry Feeling sadness, sympathy, or regret. Peter was sorry that he had been angry.

sounds Noises; things that can be heard. Nan heard cracking and creaking sounds when she was alone in the house.

south The direction to your left as you watch the sun set in the evening; toward or in the south. A south wind comes from the direction south.

spe·cial Different from others in a certain way; not ordinary; unusual. Sally wanted to find a special present for her mother's birthday.

spend To pay out money; to pass time; to use up. Father had to spend a lot of money to fix the car.

spin·ning wheel A large wheel and a spindle on a stand. What does the woman spin on the spinning wheel?

splash·es Sounds made by something hitting water or another liquid; throws water or another liquid about. The splashes of the fish made us all wet.

stand To be upright on one's feet; to be or put upright; to put up with; bear. Mother can't stand too much noise.

stared Looked very hard or very long with the eyes wide open. The animal stared at the girl for a long time before it made a move.

start To set out or make a beginning on something; to put into action or set going. We will start on our trip in the morning.

stern·ly In a harsh or strict way. Father was angry, and he spoke sternly to the children.

stick·y That sticks; covered with something sticky. Our fingers were sticky from the glue.

store A place where goods are sold; to put away for future use. Dan would like to work in a shoe store.

straw The dry stalks of grains after they have been cut and threshed. The pony had a bed of straw.

street A public way in a town or city. The cars going down the street will stop at the red light.

string A thin line of twisted threads or wire. Betty tied one end of the string to the kite. She will hold the other end in her hand.

su·per·mar·ket A large store that sells food and household goods. We buy food and many other things when we go to the supermarket.

sure Having no doubt; certain to be; steady or firm. Anna was sure that her answers were right.

swam Moved about in the water by using arms or legs, or fins and tail. Jan swam to the boat and got in it.

T

ta·bles Pieces of furniture with flat tops supported by one or more legs. There were so many people for dinner that we needed two tables.

teach·er A person who gives lessons or classes. The teacher asked many questions about the story.

tel·e·phone The system for sending sound or speech over wires by means of electricity; an instrument used to send sound or speech over a distance. Peter called his friend on the telephone and spoke to him.

third Next after second; one of three equal parts. The first pencil is blue, the second is red, and the third is green.

thir·ty The number that is three times ten. Peter has thirty records in his collection.

though In spite of the fact that; but; yet; however. Though Ed got up at six o'clock, he was late for school.

through From one end or side to the other; to various parts or places in; by means of. The dog ran through the house, from one room to another.

tick·ets Cards or pieces of paper that give the persons who hold them certain rights or services. Jack and Nan had <u>tickets</u> for the Saturday show.

tie To fasten or attach with a bow or knot. We will use string to <u>tie</u> the box.

toast Sliced bread that has been browned by heat. Julian likes to eat <u>toast</u> and jam.

to·geth·er With one another; into one gathering or mass. Pam and Frank worked <u>together</u> to clean the room.

told Put into words; said. Jack read a book that <u>told</u> about elephants.

to·mor·row The day after today. "Go to sleep," said Father. "When you wake up, it will be <u>tomorrow</u>."

tooth·brush·es Small, narrow brushes with long handles used to clean the teeth. We bought <u>toothbrushes</u> at the drugstore.

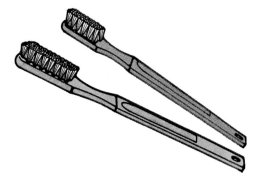

touch·es Puts the hand on or against something. Pat <u>touches</u> the feathers with his fingers to learn how they feel.

trick·y Using or marked by tricks; hard in an unexpected way; needing careful handling. Kim had a <u>tricky</u> way of finding out a secret.

tried Made an effort to do something. When Cindy <u>tried</u> to turn a cartwheel, she found that she could.

true Agreeing with the facts; not false, wrong, or made-up. It is <u>true</u> that owls have feathers.

293

tune A series of notes that make up a song or the melody of a piece of music. The old man remembered a tune he had heard long ago.

turn To move or cause to move around in a circle or part of a circle; to go or make go a certain or different way. If you turn around, you will see what is in back of you.

TV Television. John watched a news report on TV.

twen·ty Two times ten; 20. There are twenty names on Amanda's list.

type·writ·er A machine that prints letters when you hit keys. Mary wrote a letter on the typewriter.

U

Un·cle Sam A figure that represents the government or people of the United States. Uncle Sam wears red, white, and blue.

un·til Up to the time of; before. José stayed up reading until nine o'clock.

u·su·al·ly Commonly. We usually stay inside when it rains.

V

vil·lage A small group of houses; a small town. There were a shoemaker and a miller in the village.

vis·it To go or come to see. We will visit Grandmother on Sunday.

W

wag·on A vehicle that has four wheels. Mimi gave the little children a ride in the wagon.

wave To move freely back and forth or up and down; to show or signal by waving the hand; a rippling movement on the surface of water. Greg and Kim <u>wave</u> to the people on the bus.

we'll Contraction for we will; we shall. As soon as we get home <u>we'll</u> go to bed.

whale A large animal that has a body like a fish. A <u>whale</u> is not a fish, but it lives in the water.

which What one or ones; any one or ones. <u>Which</u> color do you like better, blue or red?

whole Having all its parts; entire; complete. The <u>whole</u> family will take a trip. No one will stay home.

whole·sale Of, relating to, or engaged in the selling of goods in large quantities, usually to retailers for resale. The supermarket can sell meat for more money than its <u>wholesale</u> price.

win·dow An opening in a wall or roof that lets in air and light. Beth opened her <u>window</u> before she went to bed.

wor·ry To feel or cause to feel uneasy or troubled about something. When the children did not come home for dinner, mother began to <u>worry</u> about them.

worth Good enough for; deserving of; having the same value as; the quality that makes a person or thing good or important; excellence. Pamela did not think the tickets were <u>worth</u> five dollars.

wrong Not correct or true; bad; unsuitable. The advertisement in the newspaper was <u>wrong</u>.

wrote Formed the letters, words, or symbols of something on paper or some other surface. Oliver <u>wrote</u> a letter and put it in the mail.

Y

yard An area of ground next to or surrounding a house, school, or other building. There is a big <u>yard</u> around the house where the children play.

yell To cry out loudly. "I can hear you very well," said Nan. "You don't have to <u>yell</u> so loud."

yel·low The color of gold, butter, or ripe lemons; having the color yellow. Our new car is <u>yellow</u>.

Z

ze·bra A wild animal that has a light-colored coat with black-and-white stripes. Paco said that the <u>zebra</u> looked like a pony.

This part of *Bit by Bit* is a review of letters and the sounds they stand for. Looking carefully at these letters will help you know how to say and read many new words.

Lessons

1 Initial and Final Consonants

Some words look very much the same.
Only their beginning or ending letters
are different.

| big   dig | big   bit |

You must look at word beginnings and
endings so that you do not mix up words.

A. Write a word for each picture.
Use the letters in the box to spell
the beginning sounds.

| t | d | g | b | l |

 1. ___ion    2. ___og    3. ___ird

 4. ___oad    5. ___iger    6. ___oat

298

B. Write a word for each picture. Use the
letters in the box to spell the ending sounds.

n	t	d	g	k	ck

1. ba___ **2.** du___ **3.** bu___

4. ma___ **5.** boo___ **6.** foo___

C. Number your paper from 1 to 6. Write
the following sentences. Fill in the
letters for the beginning and ending sounds.
Use the letters in the box.

g	t	l	b	d	n	k	ck

1. I always wanted a ___ittle ___og.

2. I go___ one for my ___irthday.

3. I never ___uessed that I would get a dog.

4. I have a little red he___, too.

5. She likes to ride on my dog's ba___.

6. Those two loo___ so funny.

2 Short Vowels and Graphemic Bases

Say the two words in each box. What is the same about them?

| ran | ten | box | pick | truck |
| pan | men | fox | sick | duck |

The words have the same vowel. They have the same ending sound. The words *rhyme*.

A. Number your paper from 1 to 10. Read the first word in each row. Find a word that rhymes. Write the words that rhyme on your paper.

1.	sad	sat	fed	glad
2.	clock	click	sock	luck
3.	fun	sun	fan	ten
4.	sled	bad	bed	let
5.	sit	met	sat	fit
6.	mat	fat	bit	met
7.	tag	bug	tan	rag
8.	hop	trip	stop	log
9.	cup	rip	cap	pup
10.	not	hot	top	bat

B. Number your paper from 1 to 12. Read each sentence and the words that follow it. Write the sentence using the word that makes sense.

1. The game I like best is _____. tag   top

2. I like to play with my
   _____, too. trot   truck

3. Ted can do a funny _____. trick   trip

4. He looks like a jack-in-
   the-_____. bop   box

5. I saw a _____ do a
   cartwheel. mad   man

6. I watched _____. hum   him

7. I always _____ down
   when I try. drop   drum

8. There is a park on my _____. black   block

9. We have _____ there. fan   fun

10. In the afternoon, it gets
    _____. hen   hot

11. Then we get _____ in
    the pool. wit   wet

12. I am _____ I have so
    many things to do. glen   glad

3 Initial Consonant Clusters

Look at the words in the box. Look at the
two letters at the beginning of each word.
These letters are called consonant clusters.

<u>bl</u>ack   <u>sl</u>eep   <u>pl</u>ay   <u>pr</u>etty
<u>gr</u>ass   <u>br</u>other   <u>tr</u>ip

A. Number your paper from 1 to 8. Say the
picture names. Use the letters you
underlined above to make the words.
Write the words on your paper.

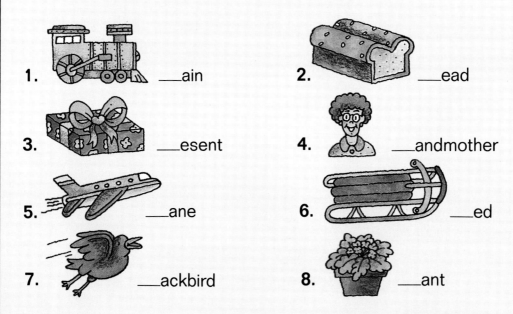

1. ___ain   2. ___ead

3. ___esent   4. ___andmother

5. ___ane   6. ___ed

7. ___ackbird   8. ___ant

B. Read the story. Number your paper from 1 to 7. Find a word in the story that begins with each pair of letters below. Write the words on your paper.

1. tr   **2.** br   **3.** pl   **4.** bl
5. gr   **6.** pr   **7.** sl

I was fishing by the lake when I heard a noise. "Who is there?" I called. "Please come out." Soon I saw a little green and blue man. "I am a troll," he said. "You should be scared!" I am brave. So I told him I was a troll, too. He slowly backed away. I felt pretty good.

C. Read the story. Find a consonant cluster for the missing letters. Write the completed paragraph on your paper.

tr   br   pl   bl
gr   pr   sl

When I am on the ___ayground I ___etend I'm a ___ackbird. I sit on the ___anch of a ___ee. I jump off and onto the ___ide. I can't really fly. I soon find myself on the ___ound. But it is fun anyway!

4 Long Vowels and Graphemic Bases

Say the two words below. You can hear the long *a* vowel sound. The underlined letters spell the long *a* vowel sound.

r<u>ai</u>n   m<u>a</u>ke

Now say the two words below. What sound do you hear? The underlined letters spell the long *i* vowel sound.

m<u>y</u>   f<u>i</u>n<u>e</u>

A. Number your paper from 1 to 12. Read each set of words. Write the word that has a long *a* or long *i* vowel sound.

1. bird	**2.** hat	**3.** bill	**4.** paint
his	late	by	easy
side	mean	city	path
5. fix	**6.** made	**7.** milk	**8.** can
five	mad	rid	cane
first	magic	nice	call
9. rip	**10.** family	**11.** braids	**12.** than
ripe	fly	branch	rain
pizza	happy	bread	card

304

B. Number your paper from 1 to 12. Write the sentences. Use a word with a long *a* or a long *i* vowel sound to finish each sentence.

1. Our new house is _____.   nice   big

2. It is by a _____.   lake   hill

3. There are _____ trees in the yard.   six   nine

4. We can _____ in them.   sit   hide

5. I like _____ new room.   my   that

6. I picked out the _____ for my room.   things   paint

7. My mom _____ shelves for my toys.   bought   made

8. There are _____ of them.   five   many

9. Mrs. Long _____ over to our house.   ran   came

10. She walks with a _____.   cane   cat

11. She gave us _____ apples from her tree.   good   ripe

12. I showed her my _____.   kite   animals

305

5 Long Vowels and Graphemic Bases

Look at the underlined letters. The long e vowel sound is spelled in two ways. Read the words.

b<u>ea</u>d   s<u>ee</u>d

Look at the spellings for the long o vowel sound. Read the words.

al<u>o</u>ne   s<u>o</u>

Which letters spell the long *u* sound in the word below?

h<u>uge</u>

A. Number your paper from 1 to 10. Read the sentence and the words that follow. Write the sentence using the word that has a long <u>e</u>, long <u>o</u>, or long <u>u</u> vowel sound.

1. I _____ to win.   run   hope
2. He can _____.   stop   read
3. Tell a _____.   joke   story
4. A _____ lives with the king.   dog   queen
5. Lin doesn't _____ well.   feel   draw
6. You are on my _____.   team   foot

7. You can _____ on me.   jump   lean
8. I will _____ to the store.   go   hop
9. I _____ my toothbrush.   wet   use
10. A _____ swims well.   seal   fish

B. Number your paper from 1 to 9. Write the sentences. Use letters from the box to finish the words.

ole	one	een	eep

1. Dan, the dog, had a b__.
2. He dug a h__ and put it in.
3. No other dogs had s__ him do it.
4. Then Dan went off to sl__.

oke	eat	eed	eel	eet

5. Soon, Dan w__ up.
6. "I n__ my bone," he said.
7. "It will be a big tr__."
8. Dan began to f__ very good.
9. He ran as fast as his f__ would go.

6 Initial and Final Consonant Digraphs

Read the following words. See how two or three underlined letters at the beginning or end of a word make one sound.

<u>sh</u>e   <u>th</u>ought   <u>wh</u>at   <u>ch</u>icken

mu<u>ch</u>   wa<u>tch</u>   fi<u>sh</u>   mou<u>th</u>

A. Number your paper from 1 to 8. Choose underlined letters from above to finish all the words in one sentence. Write the sentence on your paper. Begin the sentence with a capital letter.

1. I ___ink ___irty people will come.
2. The ___ild wanted to ___ange his ___air.
3. ___y do you ___isper?
4. ___e ___ould wear ___oes.
5. An ostri___ is su___ a funny bird!
6. It is fooli___ not to eat fi___.
7. A mou___ has tee___ inside.
8. I got a scra___ when I tried to ca___ the ball.

308

B. Use the beginning and ending sounds in the box to make words for the sentences below.

<u>sh</u>e	<u>th</u>ing	<u>wh</u>o	<u>ch</u>air
rea<u>ch</u>	ma<u>tch</u>	fi<u>sh</u>	wi<u>th</u>

Number your paper from 1 to 9. Add letters to make a word for each sentence. Write the word on your paper.

1. In the morning, my little brother ___ook me.
2. "Get up," he ___outed.
3. "Why can't you ___isper?" I asked.
4. At breakfast, my brother ___attered.
5. "I wi___ I could go to school," he said.
6. "I would walk wi___ you.

   I want to go so mu___ !

   You would not have to wa___ me.
7. "Don't be fooli___," I said.

   "You would tou___ everything.

   You couldn't ca___ a ball."
8. "I ___ ought you would say that," he said.
9. "I will wait a ___ile.

   I will ___ow you.

   I will ___ange!"

309

7 Diphthongs

What letters spell the same sound in the first
two picture names? What letters spell the
same sound in the second two picture names?

house   flower   coin   boy

A. Number your paper from 1 to 6.
Use the letters to make a word for
each sentence. Write the words.

1. He plays with a t___.	ow	oy
2. The dog is ___t.	ou	oy
3. Come here n___.	ow	oi
4. I hear a n___se.	ou	oi
5. The c___ gives milk.	ow	oi
6. You have a nice singing v___ce.	ou	oi

B. Number your paper from 1 to 4. Read the
first word in the row. Listen for the sound
of the underlined letters. Write another
word from the row that has the same sound.

310

1. c<u>ou</u>nt   join   clown   toys
2. b<u>oy</u>s   poison   mouse   down
3. t<u>ow</u>n   joy   noise   sounds
4. n<u>oi</u>sy   brown   boy   mouth

C. Number your paper from 1 to 15. Read each riddle and the three words. Write the word that answers the riddle.

1.	A big bird	owl	oil	our
2.	To yell	shark	shout	sheet
3.	Something to play with	toss	toy	too
4.	In a piggy bank	coins	costs	cross
5.	A village	toil	tied	town
6.	One, two, three	code	count	close
7.	A color	bread	bring	brown
8.	Not quiet	notice	noisy	number
9.	How much	amount	answer	anyone
10.	Rides a horse	cover	could	cowboy
11.	A home	how	house	horn
12.	A kind of plant	flower	flew	flock
13.	Lots of water	should	shook	shower
14.	Not a girl	baby	boat	boy
15.	On a queen's head	count	coupon	crown

311